SPECIAL TOPICS IN FLUID DYNAMICS

K. O. Friedrichs

notes on mathematics and its applications

GORDON AND BREACH

SPECIAL TOPICS IN
FLUID DYNAMICS

Notes on Mathememematics and its Applications

General Editors: Jacob T. Schwartz, Courant Institute of Mathematical Sciences and Maurice Lévy, Université de Paris

E. Artin, ALGEBRAIC NUMBERS AND FUNCTIONS
R. P. Boas, COLLECTED WORKS OF HIDEHIKO YAMABE
M. Davis, FUNCTIONAL ANALYSIS
M. Davis, LECTURES ON MODERN MATHEMATICS
J. Eells, Jr., SINGULARITIES OF SMOOTH MAPS
K. O. Friedrichs, ADVANCED ORDINARY DIFFERENTIAL EQUATIONS
K. O. Friedrichs, SPECIAL TOPICS IN FLUID DYNAMICS
K. O. Friedrichs and H. N. Shapiro, INTEGRATION IN HILBERT SPACE
M. Hausner and J. T. Schwartz, LIE GROUPS; LIE ALGEBRAS
P. Hilton, HOMOTOPY THEORY AND DUALITY
F. John, LECTURES ON ADVANCED NUMERICAL ANALYSIS
H. Mullish, AN INTRODUCTION TO COMPUTER PROGRAMMING
F. Rellich, PERTURBATION THEORY
J. T. Schwartz, W* ALGEBRAS
A. Silverman, EXERCISES IN FORTRAN
J. J. Stoker, NONLINEAR ELASTICITY

Additional volumes in preparation

Special Topics in Fluid Dynamics

K. O. FRIEDRICHS

*Courant Institute of
Mathematical Sciences
New York University*

Notes by S. CIOLKOWSKI

**G
B**

GORDON AND BREACH

SCIENCE PUBLISHERS · NEW YORK · LONDON · PARIS

COPYRIGHT © 1966 BY GORDON AND BREACH
Science Publishers Inc.

Library of Congress Catalog Card Number 66-20714

Gordon and Breach, Science Publishers Inc.
150 Fifth Avenue, New York, N.Y. 10011

Distributed in France by:

Dunod Editeur
92, rue Bonaparte
Paris 6

Distributed in Canada by:

The Ryerson Press
299 Queen Street West
Toronto 2B, Ontario

Printed in Great Britain by Blackie and Son, Ltd.,
Villafield Press, Bishopbriggs, Glasgow

Editors' Preface

A large number of mathematical books begin as lecture notes; but, since mathematicians are busy, and since the labor required to bring lecture notes up to the level of perfection which authors and the public demand of formally published books is very considerable, it follows that an even larger number of lecture notes make the transition to book form only after great delay or not at all. The present lecture note series aims to fill the resulting gap. It will consist of reprinted lecture notes, edited at least to a satisfactory level of completeness and intelligibility, though not necessarily to the perfection which is expected of a book. In addition to lecture notes, the series will include volumes of collected reprints of journal articles as current developments indicate, and mixed volumes including both notes and reprints.

JACOB T. SCHWARTZ
MAURICE LÉVY

Preface

In the first part of this course on "Special Topics in Fluid Dynamics" we shall be concerned with the theory of vortex motion and those parts of airfoil theory in which vortex motion plays a dominant part. We shall first derive the basic facts of three-dimensional vortex motion, in particular, Kelvin's theorem of the conservation of circulation and the theorem of the conservation of vortex lines. Secondly, we shall treat concentrated vortex filaments, in particular, those in two-dimensional flow. Treating airfoils as vortex filaments we shall discuss the flow past airfoils near the ground and the flow past airfoils from whose trailing edge a vortex filament has left. Thirdly, we shall discuss the properties of flow involving vortex sheets; in particular, we shall derive the analogues of the two theorems mentioned above.

After describing the flow past an airfoil from whose trailing edge a vortex sheet has developed we shall discuss the approximate treatment of the flow past flat airfoils. In particular, we shall treat accelerating and oscillating motion of airfoils of infinite span. The description of oscillating airfoils, of course, is the basis of the theory of flutter. Further, we shall discuss Prandtl's theory of airfoils of finite span.

Finally, we shall take up again the motion of vortex filaments and discuss von Karman's theory of vortex sheets.

This course presupposes familiarity with the basic notions of fluid dynamics, especially with the theory of two-dimensional irrotational flow treated with the aid of complex potentials, and Kutta and Joukowski's theory of airfoils of infinite span. Nevertheless, the basic notions of fluid dymanics will shortly be summarized, primarily to introduce suitable notations.

Bibliography

Durand: *Aerodynamic Theory*, Cal. Inst. of Tech., 1943.

Lamb: *Hydrodynamics*, New York, 1945.

Milne-Thompson: *Theoretical Hydrodynamics*, New York, 1951.

Prandtl-Tietjens: *Applied Hydro- and Aero-Mechanics*, New York, 1934.

Sommerfeld: *Mechanics of Deformable Bodies*, New York, 1951.

Contents

CHAPTER I

Basic Notions

Vector notation will be used in the material that is to follow. Vectors will be denoted in general by small Roman letters $a, b, c, \ldots$, scalars by Greek letter $\alpha, \beta, \gamma, \ldots$. We denote by (a_1, a_2, a_3) the components of a vector a with respect to a coordinate system and we set

$$a = \{a_1, a_2, a_3\}$$

With two vectors

$$a = \{a_1, a_2, a_3\}, \quad = b\{b_1, b_2, b_3\}$$

we associate a scalar (ab)

$$(ab) = a_1 b_1 + a_2 b_2 + a_3 b_3$$

called the scalar product* of a with b, and a vector $[a, b]$

$$[a, b] = \{a_2 b_3 - a_3 b_2, a_3 b_1 - a_1 b_3, a_1 b_2 - a_2 b_1\}$$

called the vector product* of a with b.

Let α and β be two scalars; then

$$\alpha a = \{\alpha a_1, \alpha a_2, \alpha a_3\}$$

$$\alpha a + \beta b = \{\alpha a_1 + \beta b_1, \alpha a_2 + \beta b_2, \alpha a_3 + \beta b_3\}$$

The well-known identities

$$[a, [b, c]] = (ac)b - (ab)c \tag{1.1}$$

and
$$([a, b][c, d]) = (ac)(bd) - (ad)(bc) \tag{1.2}$$

will be used frequently.

---

* The author apologizes for not having changed this unconventional notation used in the original lecture notes.

1

Denoting by $|a|$ the length of the vector a, we have

$$|a| = \sqrt{(a_1^2 + a_2^2 + a_3^2)} = \sqrt{(a\,a)}$$

The coordinates of a point x in space will be denoted by x_1, x_2, x_3; we also use the letter x for the position vector or simply "position"

$$x = \{x_1, x_2, x_3\}$$

we shall consider functions of the point x and the time t.

We introduce the gradient

$$\nabla_i = \frac{\partial}{\partial x_i} \qquad (i = 1, 2, 3)$$

and the time differentiation

$$\nabla_t = \frac{\partial}{\partial t}$$

By the gradient we mean the vector operator

$$\text{grad} = \left\{ \frac{\partial}{\partial x_1}, \frac{\partial}{\partial x_2}, \frac{\partial}{\partial x_3} \right\} = \{\nabla_1, \nabla_2, \nabla_3\} = \nabla \qquad (1.3)$$

We recall that if e is a unit vector and $f(x_1, x_2, x_3)$ a differentiable function of (x_1, x_2, x_3) then the scalar

$$(\nabla f \cdot e)$$

is the directional derivative of f in the direction of e. By a dot we indicate* that any differential operations written to the left of the dot are not to be applied to objects written to the right of the dot. For example:

$$\nabla \phi \chi = \phi \nabla \chi + \nabla \phi \cdot \chi$$

and, if **a** is a vector,*

$$(\nabla a)\chi = (\nabla a) \cdot \chi + a(\nabla)\chi$$

We further introduce the divergence of u

$$(\nabla u) = \nabla_1 u_1 + \nabla_2 u_2 + \nabla_3 u_3 \qquad (1.4)$$

and the curl of u

$$[\nabla, u] = \{\nabla_2 u_3 - \nabla_3 u_2, \nabla_3 u_1 - \nabla_1 u_3, \nabla_1 u_2 - \nabla_2 u_1\} \qquad (1.5)$$

* The author apologizes for not having changed this unconventional notation used in the original lecture notes.

We describe the motion of a particle by giving its position x as a function $x(t)$ of t, called the "path". This is the Lagrange description of flow. The velocity vector will be denoted by

$$\nabla_t x = u = \{u_1, u_2, u_3\} \tag{1.6}$$

We shall now consider a field of flow such that there is a particle at each point x in a certain region and at each time t. The velocity of the particle which happens to be at the point x at the time t will be given by a function $u = u(x,t)$; this velocity gives the Eulerian description of the flow.

Given a function of time and position it is possible to define two types of time derivatives, one being the derivative along a particle path denoted by d/dt, the other being the derivative of the function at a point denoted by $\partial/\partial t = \Delta_t$. It is then clear that the interconnection between the two types of derivatives is

$$\frac{d}{dt} = \nabla_t + \sum_{i=1}^{3} \frac{dx_i}{dt} \frac{\partial}{\partial x_i} = \nabla_t + (u\nabla) \tag{1.7}$$

d/dt is called the material derivative. Here we have that the velocity of a particle with the path $x(t)$ is

$$\frac{dx}{dt} = \nabla_t x(t) = u[x(t), t] \tag{1.8}$$

Denote by p the pressure and by ρ the density of a fluid. In these lectures we will consider incompressible fluids only, i.e. we shall take $\rho = $ constant throughout the fluid.

Under the above assumptions the basic differential equations of fluid mechanics are the laws of conservation:

$$(\nabla u) = 0 \tag{1.9}$$
$$\text{(conservation of mass)}$$

$$\nabla_t \rho u + (\nabla u)\rho u + \nabla p = 0 \tag{1.10}$$
$$\text{(conservation of momentum)}$$

$$\nabla_t \tfrac{1}{2}\rho |u|^2 + (u\nabla)\tfrac{1}{2}\rho |u|^2 + (u\nabla)p = 0 \tag{1.11}$$
$$\text{(conservation of energy)}$$

The latter law is a consequence of the first two.

The "conservation of momentum" is another expression for Newton's second law $F = ma$ or

$$\rho \frac{du}{dt} = -\nabla p \qquad (1.12)$$

Before the above laws are derived some basic notations will be introduced. A three-dimensional domain will be denoted by $\mathscr{V}$, the element of volume by $dV = dx_1\, dx_2\, dx_3$. The boundary of $\mathscr{V}$ will be denoted by $\mathscr{B}$ with surface element dB. A two-dimensional domain will be denoted by $\mathscr{A}$ with area element dA. The boundary of $\mathscr{A}$ will be denoted by $\mathscr{C}$ with length element ds. A one-dimensional segment will be denoted by $\mathscr{S}$ with s as arc length. The unit normal vector at a point of a surface will be denoted by n; if this surface is the boundary of a region the vector n is supposed to point to the exterior of the domain. We call positive or negative the side of a surface toward which the vector n or $-n$ points.

We state two well-known integral theorems:

Gauss' Theorem

$$\int_{\mathscr{V}} (\nabla u)\, dV = \int_{\mathscr{B}} (un)\, dB \qquad (1.13)$$

Stokes' Theorem

$$\int_{\mathscr{A}} ([\nabla, u]n)\, dA = \oint_{\mathscr{C}} (u\, dx) \qquad (1.14)$$

The integration over $\mathscr{C}$ is to be performed in such a direction that the interior of the domain $\mathscr{A}$ lies to the left.

We further note that

$$\int_{\mathscr{A}} \rho(un)\, dA \qquad (1.15)$$

is the flux of mass through a surface segment $\mathscr{A}$ from negative to positive side; further

$$\int_{\mathscr{A}} \rho(un)u\, dA \qquad (1.16)$$

is the flux of momentum through a surface segment $\mathscr{A}$ from negative to positive side.

The relation

$$\int_{\mathscr{B}} \rho(un)\,dB = 0 \qquad\qquad (1.17)$$

in which $\mathscr{B}$ is the boundary of a domain $\mathscr{V}$, expresses the conservation of mass: the flux of mass out of a domain is always zero.

The integral

$$\int_{\mathscr{V}} \rho u\,dV \qquad\qquad (1.18)$$

is the total momentum contained in the region $\mathscr{V}$.

The law of conservation of momentum can be stated in the form

$$\nabla_t \int_{\mathscr{V}} \rho u\,dV + \int_{\mathscr{B}} (un)\rho u\,dB + \int_{\mathscr{B}} pn\,dB = 0 \qquad\qquad (1.19)$$

In words:

The time rate of change of momentum contained in the region $\mathscr{V}$ together with the flux of momentum out of the region $\mathscr{V}$ through its boundary $\mathscr{B}$ equals the force exerted by fluid exterior to $\mathscr{V}$ against the interior of $\mathscr{V}$.

Because of

$$\int_{\mathscr{V}} (\nabla a)dV = \int_{\mathscr{B}} (an)dB$$

relation (1.19) can be put in the form

$$\int_{\mathscr{V}} \{\nabla_t \rho u + \rho(\nabla u)u + \nabla p\}\,dV = 0$$

Since this formula holds for arbitrary domains $\mathscr{V}$ it is equivalent with

$$\nabla_t \rho u + \rho(u\nabla)u + \nabla p = 0$$

which, by (1.9), is equivalent with (1.10).

Next we note that

$$\int_{\mathscr{V}} [x, \rho u]\,dV$$

is the total moment of momentum in $\mathscr{V}$ and

$$\int_{\mathscr{B}} (un)[x, \rho u]\,dB$$

is the flux of moment of momentum outward through $\mathscr{B}$. Similar to (1.19) the conservation law

$$\nabla_t \int_{\mathscr{V}} [x, \rho u] \, dV + \int_{\mathscr{B}} (un)[x, \rho u] \, dB + \int_{\mathscr{B}} p[x, n] \, dB = 0 \qquad (1.20)$$

holds, as can easily be verified. In words:

The time rate of change of moment of momentum contained in the region $\mathscr{V}$ together with the flux of moment of momentum out of the region $\mathscr{V}$ through its boundary $\mathscr{B}$ equals the moment of the force exerted by the fluid exterior to $\mathscr{V}$ against the interior of $\mathscr{V}$.

We further note that

$$\int_{\mathscr{V}} \tfrac{1}{2}\rho |u|^2 \, dV \qquad (1.21)$$

is the total kinetic energy contained in $\mathscr{V}$,

$$\int_{\mathscr{B}} (un)\tfrac{1}{2}\rho |u|^2 \, dB \qquad (1.22)$$

is the flux of kinetic energy outward through $\mathscr{B}$,

$$\int_{\mathscr{B}} (un)p \, dB \qquad (1.23)$$

is the work per unit time done by the interior fluid on the fluid that flows outward or by the exterior fluid on the fluid that flows inward.

The law of conservation of energy then can be stated in the form

$$\nabla_t \int_{\mathscr{V}} \tfrac{1}{2}\rho |u|^2 \, dV + \int_{\mathscr{B}} (un)\tfrac{1}{2}\rho |u|^2 \, dB + \int_{\mathscr{B}} (un)p \, dB = 0 \qquad (1.24)$$

Using Gauss' Theorem we obtain the formula

$$\int_{\mathscr{V}} \{\nabla_t \tfrac{1}{2}\rho |u|^2 + (\nabla u)\tfrac{1}{2}\rho |u|^2 + (\nabla u)p\} \, dV = 0 \qquad (1.25)$$

which is equivalent to

$$\nabla_t \tfrac{1}{2}\rho |u|^2 + (\nabla u)\tfrac{1}{2}\rho |u|^2 + (\nabla u)p = 0 \qquad (1.26)$$

This formula is an immediate consequence of (1.9) and (1.10).

The type of flow for which the time derivative

$$\nabla_t q$$

of all flow quantities q is zero is called a *steady flow*.

There are several forms of *Bernoulli's law*. Its first form states that along each particle path in a steady flow the quantity

$$\tfrac{1}{2}\rho |u|^2 + p$$

is a constant. This statement follows directly from the conservation of momentum (1.10) or Newton's second law (1.12).

CHAPTER 2

Vorticity

We introduce the vector
$$g = [\nabla, u] \tag{2.1}$$
called the vorticity vector. It is clear that its divergence vanishes,
$$(\nabla g) = 0 \tag{2.2}$$
Also the formula
$$[u, g] = [u, [\nabla, u]] = \nabla(u \cdot u) - (u\nabla)u = \tfrac{1}{2}\nabla(u\,u) - (u\nabla)u \tag{2.3}$$
is useful. Using the expression $(u\nabla)u$ from the above formula in the laws of conservation of momentum and mass [cf. (1.9), (1.10)] we obtain the relation
$$\rho\nabla_t u + \rho\{\tfrac{1}{2}\nabla(u\,u) - [u, g]\} + \nabla p = 0 \tag{2.4}$$

From equation (2.4) we shall read off the second Bernoulli law and laws about the vorticity vector.

The flow is called *irrotational* if the vorticity vanishes, $g = 0$; for such flow there exists a function $\phi(x)$ such that the velocity is its gradient
$$u = \nabla\phi; \tag{2.5}$$
ϕ is called the velocity potential. Inserting $g = 0$ in (2.4) we get
$$\nabla(\rho\nabla_t \phi + \tfrac{1}{2}\rho\,|u|^2 + p) = 0 \tag{2.6}$$
or
$$\rho\nabla_t \phi + \tfrac{1}{2}\rho\,|u|^2 + p = \text{constant}; \tag{2.7}$$

this is called *Bernoulli's second law* valid for irrotational flow. For steady flow it reduces to
$$\tfrac{1}{2}\rho\,|u|^2 + p = \text{constant}$$

Here the constant refers to the whole field of flow.

More generally by taking the curl of relation (2.4) we get

$$\nabla_t g - [\nabla, [u, g]] = 0 \qquad (2.8)$$

or

$$\nabla_t g - (\nabla g)u + (\nabla u)g = 0 \qquad (2.9)$$

or upon using the laws of conservation of mass and (2.1)

$$\nabla_t g + (u\nabla)g - (g\nabla)u = 0 \qquad (2.10)$$

This formula can also be written in the form

$$\frac{dg}{dt} = (g\nabla)u \qquad (2.11)$$

The last formula implies that if g were zero to begin with then $g = 0$ at all times. In other words, if the flow was irrotational at some time it will remain irrotational. Relation (2.11) was made the basis of a theory of vortex flow by Helmholtz.

We define the *circulation* $C_{\mathscr{C}}$ of a closed curve $\mathscr{C}$ to be

$$C_{\mathscr{C}} = \oint_{\mathscr{C}} (u\,dx) \qquad (2.12)$$

From the integral theorems (1.13), (1.14) we have

$$C_{\mathscr{C}} = \int_{\mathscr{A}} ([\nabla, u]n)\,dA = \int_{\mathscr{A}} (gn)\,dA$$

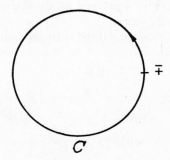

Fig. 2.1.

provided $\mathscr{C}$ is the boundary of a region $\mathscr{A}$. Consequently the circulation is zero if $g = 0$. In a multiply connected region, $C_{\mathscr{C}}$ may be different from zero, if the curve $\mathscr{C}$ is not the boundary of a region $\mathscr{A}$.

In terms of a velocity potential ϕ we have

$$C_{\mathscr{C}} = \oint_{\mathscr{C}} (u\,dx) = \phi\,|\,{}^+_-\,;$$

in this case therefore $C_{\mathscr{C}}$ is the jump in potential, see Fig. 2.1.

We proceed to derive *two basic theorems about vortex motion.* In a field of flow consider a closed curve $\mathscr{C}(t) = x(t, \sigma)$ composed of certain particles having a label $\sigma, \sigma_- \leqq \sigma \leqq \sigma_+$. We assume $x(t, \sigma_+) = x(t, \sigma_-)$. Then these particles will form a closed curve which we denote by $\mathscr{C}(t) = x(t, \sigma)$, see Fig. 2.2. We then consider the circulation of $\mathscr{C}(t)$

$$C_{\mathscr{C}(t)} = \int_{\sigma_-}^{\sigma_+} (u(x(t, \sigma), t), \nabla_\sigma x(t, \sigma))\,d\sigma$$

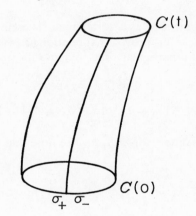

Fig. 2.2.

Its derivative is

$$\frac{d}{dt} C_{\mathscr{C}}(t) = \int_{\sigma_-}^{\sigma_+} (\{\nabla_t u + (\nabla u)u\} \cdot \nabla_\sigma x(t, \sigma))\,d\sigma + \int_{\sigma_-}^{\sigma_+} (u \nabla_\sigma u)\,d\sigma$$

which by (1.10) becomes

$$\frac{d}{dt} C_{\mathscr{C}}(t) = \int_{\sigma_-}^{\sigma_+} \left\{ -\frac{1}{\rho}\frac{dp}{d\sigma} + \frac{1}{2}\frac{du^2}{d\sigma} \right\} d\sigma = \tfrac{1}{2}u^2 - \frac{1}{\rho}p\,\bigg|_{\sigma_-}^{\sigma_+} = 0$$

or
$$C_{\mathscr{C}}(t) = \text{constant} \qquad\qquad (2.13)$$

Thus we have proved

Kelvin's Theorem: If a circuit moves so that it is always formed by the same particles, its circulation remains unchanged.

A *vortex line or vortex segment* is a segment such that the vorticity vector g at each point of the segment is tangent to the segment at that point. We shall prove now that if a segment is a vortex line at a particular time t then the segment formed by the same particles at a later time is also a vortex line.

Let the segment $\mathscr{S} = \mathscr{S}(t)$ be described parametrically by $x(t, \sigma)$, $\sigma_- \leqq \sigma \leqq \sigma_+$, where σ is a label for the particles composing the segment. Then the relation

$$[g,\ \nabla_\sigma\ x] = 0 \tag{2.14}$$

characterizes the segment $\mathscr{S}$ as a vortex line. Therefore, the statement is established as soon as it is proved that relation (2.14) holds at all times whenever it holds at a particular time. We use the abbreviation

$$y = \nabla_\sigma x = \nabla_\sigma x(t, \sigma) \tag{2.15}$$

and
$$z = [y, g] = [\nabla_\sigma x, g] = [\nabla_\sigma x(t, \sigma), g(x(t, \sigma), t)] \tag{2.16}$$

and form the material derivative dz/dt. We note that the derivative of $y = \nabla_\sigma x(t, \sigma)$ is

$$\frac{dy}{dt} = \frac{d}{dt}\nabla_\sigma x(t, \sigma) = \nabla_\sigma \nabla_t x(t, \sigma) = \nabla_\sigma u(x(t, \sigma), t)$$

$$= (\nabla_\sigma x(t, \sigma) \cdot \nabla)u(x(t, \sigma), t)$$

or
$$\frac{dy}{dt} = (y\nabla)u \tag{2.17}$$

while according to (2.11) the material derivative of $g(x(t, \sigma), t)$ is

$$\frac{d}{dt}g(x(t, \sigma), t) = (g(x(t, \sigma), t)\nabla)u(x(t, \sigma), t)$$

or
$$\frac{dg}{dt} = (g\nabla)u \tag{2.18}$$

Thus we find

$$\frac{dz}{dt} = [(y\nabla)u; g] + [y, (g\nabla)u]$$
$$= [y, (g\nabla)u] - [g, (y\nabla)u] \tag{2.19}$$

We maintain that this relation reduces to

$$\frac{dz}{dt} = [[[g, y], \nabla], u] \tag{2.20}$$

If a proper vector d were taken instead of the symbol ∇, the scalar products (gd) and (yd) would be numbers and the right-hand member could be written in the form

$$[(gd)y, u] - [(yd)g, u]$$

This expression now equals the expression

$$[[[g, y], d], u]$$

by virtue of identity (1.1). This identity remains valid if d is replaced by the differential operator ∇ provided that this operator acts only on the function u and not on g and y. This condition is met by the position which ∇ has on the right member of (2.20). This relation is thus seen to hold.

Using the definition (2.16) of z we can write this relation in the form

$$\frac{dz}{dt} = -[[z, \nabla], u] \tag{2.21}$$

The components of the right member here are linear combinations of the components of z with coefficients which are linear combinations of the derivatives of the components of u. In any case relation (2.21) may be written in the form

$$\frac{dz}{dt} = Az \tag{2.22}$$

with an appropriate matrix A. This matrix is a known function of t and σ inasmuch as $u = u(x(t, \sigma), t)$ and the derivatives of u are known functions of t and σ. Relation (2.22) can thus be considered a linear homogeneous differential equation. It follows from the theory of such differential equations that the function $z(t)$ vanishes for all times if it vanishes at one time.

Now, our only assumption was that the vector z was zero along the segment $\mathscr{S}$ at a certain time. It thus follows that z vanishes at all times and our statement is proved.

Finally, we introduce the notion of *vortex tube*. Such a tube is generated by a set of vortex segments whose end points form closed circuits. We first state that the circulation of any two circuits around the vortex tube is the same provided the two circuits are such that they can be deformed into each other. Consequently, we can speak of *the circulation of the vortex tube*. The statement follows from Stokes' theorem (1.14) applied to the piece $\mathscr{A}$ of the surface of the tube which is bounded by the two circuits. For, this theorem states that the difference of the two circulations equals the integral of the normal component of the vorticity over $\mathscr{A}$. Now this normal component vanishes on each point of the tube since the vorticity vector, having the direction of a generating vortex segment is tangential to the tube surface.

In this argument it is tacitly assumed that the two circuits do not intersect. Otherwise the argument must be somewhat modified.

Combining the statement just made with the two theorems formulated before, we may say:

A tube moving so that it is always formed by the same particles remains a vortex tube if it once was a vortex tube, and its circulation remains unchanged.

Stream Vector. Biot-Savart Formula

We add a few items in this chapter 2 which are useful but not essential in the following.

We first note that it is possible to express the velocity vector as the curl of another vector

$$\psi = \{\psi_1, \psi_2, \psi_3\}$$

in the form
$$u = [\nabla, \psi] \qquad (2.23)$$

This can be done since the divergence of u vanishes. The flux of volume through a surface $\mathscr{A}$ with the boundary $\mathscr{B}$ can then be expressed as

$$\int_{\mathscr{A}} (un)\, dA = \oint (\psi\, dx)$$

as seen from Stokes' theorem. We shall call ψ a "stream vector". The reason is that in two-dimensional flow a stream vector of the form $\psi = \{0, 0, \psi_3\}$ can be found, whose component ψ_3 is the stream function of that flow. Also in rotationally symmetric flow a stream vector can be found which has only a component in the direction perpendicular to the axis; except for a factor this component is Stokes' stream function.

The stream vector is not unique. It can be shown that it can always be so determined that

$$(\nabla\psi) = 0 \tag{2.24}$$

The vorticity of the flow is easily expressed in terms of the stream vector as

$$g = -\nabla^2 \psi \tag{2.25}$$

where $\nabla^2 = (\nabla\nabla) =$ div grad. This fact follows from the relation

$$g = [\nabla, [\nabla, \psi]] = \nabla(\nabla\psi) - (\nabla\nabla)\psi = -(\nabla\nabla)\psi$$

The relation $g = -\nabla^2\psi$ enables us to express the stream vector ψ in terms of the vorticity vector g provided the flow is defined in the whole space $\mathcal{V}_\infty$ and attains a velocity U_∞ as $|x| \to \infty$ in any direction. We then have

$$\psi(x) = \frac{1}{4\pi} \int_{\mathcal{V}_\infty} |x'-x|^{-1} g(x')\,dV' + \tfrac{1}{3}[U_\infty, x] \tag{2.26}$$

It is known that the first term here represents the solution of the equation $\nabla^2\psi = -g$ which vanishes at ∞ provided $g(x)$ dies out sufficiently as $|x| \to \infty$. From

$$[\nabla, [U_\infty, x]] = (\nabla x)U_\infty - x(\nabla U_\infty) = (\nabla x)U_\infty = 3U_\infty \tag{2.27}$$

it is clear that the term $\tfrac{1}{3}[U_\infty, x]$ contributes the velocity U_∞ at ∞.

The velocity u can be obtained from the formula for ψ by taking the curl of ψ, thus

$$u(x) = \frac{1}{4\pi} \int_{\mathcal{V}_\infty} |x'-x|^{-3} [(x'-x), g(x')]\,dV' + U_\infty \tag{2.28}$$

This formula is essentially Biot-Savart's formula in electro-magnetic theory. It enables us to determine the velocity in terms of the vorticity. Of course this formula is not sufficient to solve flow problems; for, the relation

$$\frac{dg}{dt} = (g\nabla)u \tag{2.29}$$

should be satisfied.

The latter condition can be given a very concise form in case the flow is two-dimensional and steady. In that case the stream vector $\psi = \{0, 0, \psi_3\}$ and the vorticity vector $g = \{0, 0, g_3\}$ have only one component which depends only on (x_1, x_2). Thus the condition $(\nabla\psi) = 0$ is satisfied automatically and

$$u_1 = \nabla_2 \psi_3, \quad u_2 = -\nabla_1 \psi_3$$

Evidently, $(g\nabla)u = 0$ and hence equation (2.29) becomes

$$(u\nabla)g = 0$$

or

$$\nabla_2 \psi_3 \nabla_1 g_3 - \nabla_1 \psi_3 \nabla_2 g_3 = 0$$

This equation is satisfied if and only if a function $f(\psi_3)$ exists such that

$$g_3 = f(\psi_3)$$

or

$$\nabla^2 \psi_3 = -f(\psi_3) \tag{2.30}$$

The flow problem is thus reduced to solving differential equations of the form (2.30). If this equation has been solved for an arbitrary function f then a flow has been found.

Irrotational flow—Complex potential

A flow is called irrotational if the vorticity vanishes everywhere except possibly on lines and surfaces. As mentioned above the velocity can then be derived from a potential $\phi = \phi(x)$

$$u = \nabla\phi \tag{2.31}$$

Two-dimensional irrotational flows can be described with the aid of analytic functions of the complex variable

$$z = x_1 + ix_2 \tag{2.32}$$

With the aid of the "stream function" $\psi = \psi_3(x_1, x_2)$ we form the "complex velocity potential"

$$\chi = \phi + i\psi \tag{2.33}$$

The relations

$$u_1 = \nabla_1 \phi = \nabla_2 \psi$$
$$u_2 = \nabla_2 \phi = -\nabla_1 \psi$$

tell us that χ is an analytic function of z and that the derivative of χ is connected with the velocity through the relation

$$\frac{d\chi}{dz} = u_1 - iu_2 \tag{2.34}$$

Contrary to custom we shall use the letter w to designate the combination

$$w = u_1 + iu_2 \tag{2.35}$$

so that the complex conjugate

$$\overline{w} = u_1 - iu_2 \tag{2.36}$$

and not w, is an analytic function of z.

We note that also unsteady irrotational flow can be described by a complex potential χ, which then also depends on the time t. Bernoulli's law (2.7) then expresses the relationship between pressure and velocity.

The circulation of a circuit $\mathscr{C}$ which encloses a region in which the flow is not irrotational is given by

$$C_{\mathscr{C}} = \int_{\mathscr{C}} \overline{w}\, dz$$

The imaginary part of this integral is the flux through the circuit $\mathscr{C}$, and hence vanishes assuming that no sources or sinks are present inside of $\mathscr{C}$.

CHAPTER 3

Vortex Filaments

The investigation of vortex flow is greatly facilitated if one considers flows which are irrotational except for lines or surfaces at which vorticity is concentrated. A vortex filament $\mathscr{L}$ in an otherwise irrotational flow is characterized by the condition that the circulation of any circuit surrounding the line is different from zero. Clearly the circulation is the same for any two circuits which can be deformed into each other.

The simplest vortex filaments are those occurring in two-dimensional irrotational flow. We describe the flow with the aid of a complex potential χ of the complex variable z. A straight vortex filament passing through the point $z = z_{\mathscr{L}}$ is present in the flow if the circulation

$$C = \int_{\mathscr{C}} \bar{w}\, dz \qquad (3.1)$$

of a circuit $\mathscr{C}$ surrounding the point $z_{\mathscr{L}}$ is different from zero. More specifically whenever we speak of a vortex filament in two-dimensional flow we shall imply that the complex potential $\chi(z)$ of the flow is of the form

$$\chi(z) = \frac{C}{2\pi i}\log(z - z_{\mathscr{L}}) + \chi_R(z) \qquad (3.2)$$

in which the function $\chi_R(z)$ is regular at $z = z_{\mathscr{L}}$.

The complex velocity, given by

$$\bar{w} = \frac{d\chi}{dz} \qquad (3.3)$$

is then, in obvious notation,

$$\bar{w} = \frac{C}{2\pi i(z - z_{\mathscr{L}})} + \bar{w}_R \qquad (3.4)$$

19

A vortex filament may be "bound" or "free". It is called bound if it is the idealization of a thin material cylinder, which is able to suffer and exert forces. The filament is called free if it is the idealization of a thin cylinder of fluid which, in the limit, cannot sustain forces. The condition that a free vortex does not sustain forces must be used in order to determine its motion.

In order to calculate the force exerted by the fluid on the vortex filament, we observe the flow from a frame which moves with such a constant velocity that the vortex filament is at rest at the time considered. Then we place a circuit $\mathscr{C}$ around the point $z_{\mathscr{L}}$ and determine the force exerted by the fluid on the filament as the force exerted by the exterior on the cylinder through $\mathscr{C}$ and the sum of the flux of momentum out of this cylinder and the rate of change of momentum in the interior $\mathscr{R}$ of the cylinder. All these quantities will be taken per unit length in direction of the x_3 axis. The rate of change of momentum per unit length in $\mathscr{R}$ is

$$\nabla_t \int_{\mathscr{R}} \int \rho u \, dx_1 \, dx_2 = \rho \int_{\mathscr{R}} \int \nabla_t u \, dx_1 \, dx_2$$

since as assumed, the vortex point does not move at the time considered. The desired force per unit length is, therefore, found as

$$F = -\rho \int_{\mathscr{R}} \int \nabla_t u \, dx_1 \, dx_2 - \int_{\mathscr{C}} \{pn + \rho u(un)\} \, ds$$

or, after using Bernoulli's law (2.7), as

$$F = -\rho \int_{\mathscr{R}} \int \nabla_t u \, dx_1 \, dx_2 + \tfrac{1}{2}\rho \int_{\mathscr{C}} \{|u|^2 n - 2u(un)\} \, ds + \rho \int_{\mathscr{C}} \nabla_t \phi n \, ds$$

From the assumption that the vortex point $z_{\mathscr{L}}$ is at rest at the time considered we deduce that only the regular part χ_R of χ contributes to the terms $\nabla_t u$ and $\nabla_t \phi$. By virtue of Gauss' formula we then obtain

$$-\int_{\mathscr{R}} \int \nabla_t u \, dx_1 \, dx_2 + \int_{\mathscr{C}} \nabla_t \phi n \, ds$$

$$= -\int_{\mathscr{R}} \int \nabla_t u_R \, dx_1 \, dx_2 + \int_{\mathscr{C}} \nabla_t \phi_R n \, ds = 0$$

Thus we obtain the expression

$$F = \tfrac{1}{2}\rho \int_{\mathscr{C}} \{|u|^2 n - 2u(un)\}\, ds \tag{3.5}$$

for the force F.

This expression can be elegantly written in terms of a complex integral of an analytic function of the complex variable $z = x_1 + ix_2$. In addition to the complex velocity $w = u_1 + iu_2$ we introduce the complex force

$$H = F_1 + iF_2$$

In terms of the components n_1, n_2 of the normal vector n we have

$$n_1\, ds = dx_2, \quad n_2\, ds = -dx_1$$

and hence

$$(n_1 + in_2)\, ds = -i\, dz, \quad (n_1 - in_2)\, ds = i\, d\bar{z}$$

Further we have

$$(un)\, ds = u_1\, dx_2 - u_2\, dx_1 = \operatorname{Im} \bar{w}\, dz = \frac{i}{2}(w\, d\bar{z} - \bar{w}\, dz)$$

Instead of (3.5) we therefore may write

$$H = \tfrac{1}{2}\rho \int_{\mathscr{C}} \{-iw\bar{w}\, dz - iw(w\, d\bar{z} - \bar{w}\, dz)\}$$

or

$$H = -\frac{i}{2}\rho \int_{\mathscr{C}} w^2\, d\bar{z} \tag{3.6}$$

The complex conjugate of this expression

$$\bar{H} = \frac{i}{2}\rho \int_{\mathscr{C}} \bar{w}^2\, dz \tag{3.7}$$

is the integral over the analytic function $\bar{w}^2$ of the complex variable z.

This integral can be evaluated by virtue of relation (3.4) which is a consequence of assumption (3.2). Since the analytic function $\bar{w}_R$ is regular at $z = z_{\mathscr{L}}$ we have

$$\int_{\mathscr{C}} \bar{w}_R^2\, dz = 0;$$

also

$$\int_{\mathscr{C}} \frac{dz}{(z - z_{\mathscr{L}})^2} = 0$$

2

We thus obtain from (3.7) and (3.4) the expression

$$\bar{H} = \frac{C\rho}{2\pi} \int_{\mathscr{C}} \frac{\bar{w}_R}{z - z_{\mathscr{L}}} dz$$

Again, because of the regularity of $w_R(z)$ at $z = z_{\mathscr{L}}$, the integral here is nothing but the value of $\bar{w}_R(z)$ at $z = z_{\mathscr{L}}$. Thus we obtain the formula

$$\bar{H} = i\rho C \, \bar{w}_R(z_{\mathscr{L}})$$

or
$$H = -i\rho C w_R(z_{\mathscr{L}}) \qquad (3.8)$$

This formula was derived under the assumption that the vortex point does not move at the time considered. This situation can be brought about by observing the flow from a frame that moves with a constant velocity which equals the velocity $dx_{\mathscr{L}}/dt$ of the vortex point at the time considered. Observed from this frame the flow velocity is $u - dx_{\mathscr{L}}/dt$ where u is the actual flow velocity. The corresponding complex quantity is $w - dz_{\mathscr{L}}/dt$. Consequently, instead of formula (3.8) the formula

$$H = -i\rho C \left\{ w_R(z_{\mathscr{L}}) - \frac{dz_{\mathscr{L}}}{dt} \right\} \qquad (3.9)$$

holds in general. In vectorial fashion this formula may be written as

$$F = -\rho \left[G, \left\{ u_R(x_{\mathscr{L}}) - \frac{dx_{\mathscr{L}}}{dt} \right\} \right] \qquad (3.10)$$

in which $G = \{0, 0, C\}$ is the vector in direction of the vortex filament having the circulation as its magnitude.

Formula (3.9) or (3.10) is similar to that of Kutta and Joukowski for steady flow past a profile. The difference is that the relative regular part of the velocity $u_{\mathscr{R}}(x_{\mathscr{L}}) - dx_{\mathscr{L}}/dt$ takes the place of the velocity at infinity in the steady flow.

The regular part $u_{\mathscr{R}}(x_{\mathscr{L}})$ of the velocity can be defined without reference to the description (3.2) of the flow, as the limit of a mean value

$$u_{\mathscr{R}}(x_{\mathscr{L}}) = \lim_{r \to 0} \frac{1}{2\pi r} \int_{|x - x_{\mathscr{L}}| = r} u(x)\, ds \qquad (3.11)$$

This definition is even applicable to general vortex filaments in the three-dimensional flow. The force per unit length F exerted by the fluid on a point of the vortex filament is then also given by formula (3.10) when the vectors occurring in this formula are taken as the appropriate three-dimensional vectors.

A vortex filament was called *bound* if it can sustain a force; a bound vortex filament actually occurs only as the limit of a filament consisting of solid matter.

A vortex point was called *free* if it can not sustain a force. Vortex filaments in a fluid not consisting of solid matter are free. Assuming that the circulation C does not vanish we see from formula (3.10) that the relation

$$\frac{dx_{\mathscr{L}}}{dt} = u_R(x_{\mathscr{L}}) \qquad (3.12)$$

or

$$\frac{dz_{\mathscr{L}}}{dt} = u_R(z_{\mathscr{L}}) \qquad (3.13)$$

holds for a free vortex. This formula may be interpreted as a *differential equation* for the position $x_{\mathscr{L}} = x_{\mathscr{L}}(t)$ of the vortex point. It is most remarkable that the differential equation governing the motion of a free vortex is of the *first order* and not of the second order as the differential equations governing the motion of particles in Mechanics.

As a typical example we consider a pair of free vortex filaments in two-dimensional flow placed at the point $z^{(1)}$ and $z^{(2)}$. Assuming that the flow velocity at infinity is a constant U^{∞} the complex potential of the flow becomes

$$\chi(z) = \frac{C_1}{2\pi i}\log(z - z^{(1)}) + \frac{C_2}{2\pi i}\log(z - z^{(2)}) + \overline{W}^{\infty} z$$

From

$$\overline{w} = \frac{d\chi}{dz} = \frac{C_1}{2\pi i}(z - z^{(1)})^{-1} + \frac{C_2}{2\pi i}(z - z^{(2)})^{-1} + \overline{W}^{\infty}$$

we extract the regular parts

$$w_R(z^{(1)}) = \frac{C_2 i}{2\pi}(\bar{z}^{(1)} - \bar{z}^{(2)})^{-1} + \overline{W}^{\infty}$$

$$w_R(z^{(2)}) = \frac{C_1 i}{2\pi}(\bar{z}^{(2)} - \bar{z}^{(1)})^{-1} + \overline{W}^{\infty}$$

The differential equations of motion are

$$\frac{dz^{(1)}}{dt} = \frac{C_2\,i}{2\pi}(\bar{z}^{(1)} - \bar{z}^{(2)})^{-1} + \overline{W}^{\infty}$$

$$\frac{dz^{(2)}}{dt} = \frac{C_1\,i}{2\pi}(\bar{z}^{(2)} - \bar{z}^{(1)})^{-1} + \overline{W}^{\infty}$$

It is not difficult to solve these equations. Problems of this type will be treated in the next section and also in a later section.

CHAPTER 4

Airfoils as Vortex Filaments

As we know from the theory of two-dimensional potential flow, the most outstanding feature of the flow past an infinite airfoil of constant profile is the circulation around it. This circulation is the principal factor determining the lift force exerted by the fluid on the airfoil. For many purposes it is a sufficient approximation to consider the airfoil as just a vortex filament with the appropriate circulation. We shall here discuss several problems in which this approximation gives useful information.

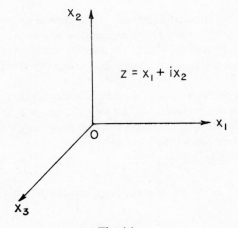

Fig. 4.1.

We consider first the almost trivial problem of an infinite airfoil in parallel flow. We suppose that in this approximation the airfoil is the x_3 axis and we look at the flow in the (x_1, x_2) plane, see Fig. 4.1. We assume that at infinity the velocity is $(U, 0)$ and that the circulation

25

about the origin is C. We then know that the complex velocity potential becomes

$$\chi(z) = Uz + \frac{C}{2\pi i}\log z \tag{4.1}$$

from which we have

$$\frac{d\chi}{dz} = u - iv = U + \frac{C}{2\pi i}\frac{1}{z} \tag{4.2}$$

The complex force H on the airfoil then becomes (cf. chapter 3)

$$H = F_1 + iF_2 = -i\rho C \frac{(d\chi)}{(dz)}R$$

where $(d\chi)/(dz)R$ is the "regular part" of $d\chi/dz$ at the point $z = 0$ introduced in chapter 3. As seen from (4.2) its regular part is U. Hence

$$H = iF_2$$

with
$$F_2 = -\rho CU \tag{4.3}$$

We thus see that the airfoil moves in the direction of the negative or positive x_2 axis according as the circulation is positive or negative.

Formula (4.3) for the "lift" F_2 agrees with that of Kutta and Joukowski since the regular velocity U is at the same time the velocity at infinity.

The second problem has to do with the description of *the flow past an airfoil near the ground*. We assume the ground to be the (x_1, x_3) plane, the airfoil to be located on the line $x_1 = 0, x_2 = h$ or in terms of the complex variable $z = x_1 + ix_2$ at

$$z = ih$$

We assume the airfoil to be stationary and the flow to have at infinity the velocity

$$u_1 = U, \quad u_2 = 0$$

or with $w = u + iv$

$$w = U \quad \text{at} \quad z = \infty$$

The circulation of the airfoil will be denoted by $C = -\Gamma$; we assume $\Gamma > 0$.

We describe the flow with the aid of a complex velocity potential $\chi(z)$ which should have the properties:

1. $\bar{w} = d\chi/dz \to U$ as $z \to \infty$, i.e. the flow velocity approaches the value U at infinity.

2. $\chi(z) + (\Gamma/2\pi i)\log(z-ih)$ is regular at $z = ih$; i.e. the flow has a vortex with the circulation $-\Gamma$ at the point $z = ih$.

3. $\chi(z)$ is real for real z.

The latter property expresses the condition that the x_1 axis is a stream line, see Fig. 4.2.

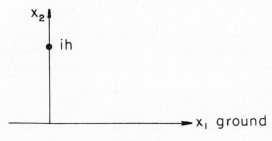

Fig. 4.2.

We obtain the function $\chi(z)$ by reflecting the flow in the x_1 axis. The reflected function is given by $\chi(\bar{z}) = \overline{\chi(z)}$. The continued flow evidently has a vortex point at $z = -ih$ with the circulation $C = +\Gamma$. By superimposing pure vortex flow at $z = \pm ih$ with parallel flow we obtain the complex velocity potential

$$\chi(z) = Uz - \frac{\Gamma}{2\pi i}\log(z-ih) + \frac{\Gamma}{2\pi i}\log(z+ih) \tag{4.4}$$

which has all desired properties, as can be immediately verified.

We are primarily interested in the force H exerted by the fluid on the airfoil. According to the theory developed in chapter 3 we should calculate the regular part of the complex velocity w of the flow at $z = ih$.
Evidently

$$\bar{w} = \frac{d\chi}{dz} = U + \frac{\Gamma}{2\pi i}\frac{1}{z+ih} - \frac{\Gamma}{2\pi i}\frac{1}{z-ih} \tag{4.5}$$

$$\bar{w}_R(ih) = U + \frac{\Gamma}{i4\pi ih}$$

$$w_R(ih) = U - \frac{\Gamma}{4\pi h} \tag{4.6}$$

Since the complex force $G = F_1 + iF_2$ is given by

$$H = -i\rho C w_R(ih) \tag{4.7}$$

we conclude from (4.5) that $H = iF_2$ with

$$F_2 = \rho\Gamma\left(U - \frac{\Gamma}{4\pi h}\right) \tag{4.8}$$

We thus see that the effect of the ground is to diminish the lift F_2 as if the velocity of the flow at infinity were $U - \Gamma/4\pi h$ instead of U. Metaphorically speaking, we may also say that the ground effectively attracts the airfoil.

Thus far our attitude has been that the airfoil has a given circulation. Aerodynamicists however take a different attitude.

According to the theory of airfoils in a flow without obstacles, the lift F_2 experienced by the airfoil is given by formula

$$F_2 = \rho\Gamma U \tag{4.9}$$

of Kutta and Joukowski, in which $\Gamma = -C$ is the counter circulation and U is the flow velocity at infinity. The counter circulation Γ in its turn depends on the velocity U according to the formula

$$\Gamma = \tau U \tag{4.10}$$

in which the factor τ depends on the shape and the position of the airfoil, essentially on the depth t and the angle of attack α, see Fig. 4.3,

$$\tau = \tau(t, \alpha)$$

In the present problem the lift force is also given by formula (4.9) with the one difference that the regular part of the velocity plays the role of the velocity at infinity.

That this should be so could be motivated by the following arguments. If the dimensions of the airfoil are small compared with its height above the ground the regular part of the velocity does not vary very much over a region large compared with the dimension of the airfoil. We can thus be sure that our formula (4.8) gives a good approximation at large heights compared with the dimensions of the airfoil if the proper circulation is taken.

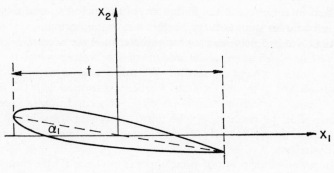

Fig. 4.3.

Aerodynamicists now adopt the same formula for the lift that is valid in flow without obstacles but substitute for U the regular part of the velocity at the airfoil. In the present problem the counter circulation Γ is thus given by

$$\Gamma = \tau \left[U - \frac{\Gamma}{4\pi h} \right] \tag{4.11}$$

Solving equation (4.11) for Γ we get

$$\Gamma = \frac{hU\tau}{h + \tau/4\pi} \tag{4.12}$$

The regular part of the velocity becomes from (4.6)

$$U - \frac{\Gamma}{4\pi h} = \frac{h}{h + \tau/4\pi} U \tag{4.13}$$

and hence formula (4.8) gives

$$F_2 = \frac{\rho \tau U^2 h^2}{(h + \tau/4\pi)^2} \tag{4.14}$$

for the lift.

From this formula it is seen that the lift F_2 is always positive and approaches zero as the height of the airfoil above the ground approaches zero.

In flow past actual airfoils the effect here described is in general overshadowed by the effect of the finite span of the airfoil so that the actual lift may be larger than at large heights above the ground.

As the third problem we propose to determine *the potential flow past an airfoil in which there is an additional free vortex with circulation opposite to that around the airfoil*. We know that in accelerating the airfoil from rest to its final velocity vorticity is formed near the trailing edge until the Kutta condition is satisfied. This condition requires that the velocity at the trailing edge be finite (otherwise the velocity would be infinite and the velocity gradient would become infinite forcing viscosity to act).

A simplified description of what appears once the Kutta condition is satisfied is that a single vortex filament leaves the trailing edge and moves into the fluid behind the airfoil. From Kelvin's theorem it is clear that the circulation of this single vortex is opposite to that of the flow around the airfoil since at the beginning of the motion the circulation over a large contour containing the airfoil was zero. We assume the airfoil to be stationary at the point $z = 0$; the location of the free vortex will be denoted by $z^0(t)$, the velocity at infinity is assumed to be $w = (U, 0)$. The circulation of the airfoil is $C = -\Gamma$, the complex velocity potential $\chi(z)$ is evidently

$$\chi(z) = Uz - \frac{\Gamma}{2\pi i}\log z + \frac{\Gamma}{2\pi i}\log(z - z^0(t)) \qquad (4.15)$$

Of course, the flow is not steady. The velocity of the free vortex is given by

$$\frac{dz^0}{dt} = w_R(z^0(t)) = w_R(t) \qquad (4.16)$$

(cf. chapter 3). Since

$$\bar{w} = \frac{dx}{dz} = U - \frac{\Gamma}{2\pi i z} + \frac{\Gamma}{2\pi i(z - z^0(t))} \qquad (4.17)$$

we have

$$\bar{w}_R(t) = U - \frac{\Gamma}{2\pi i z^0(t)}$$

and we get

$$\frac{dz^0}{dt} = U + \frac{\Gamma}{2\pi i \bar{z}^0} \qquad (4.18)$$

This differential equation can be solved in a certain sense. We split the differential equation into real and imaginary parts setting $|z^0| = r_0$ and $\Gamma = 2\pi\gamma U$. We get

$$\frac{dx_1^0}{dt} = U + \frac{\gamma U x_2^0}{r_0^2} \qquad (4.19)$$

$$\frac{dx_2^0}{dt} = -\gamma U \frac{x_1^0}{r_0^2} \qquad (4.20)$$

$$\frac{dr_0}{dt} = \frac{x_1^0 \dfrac{dx_1^0}{dt} + x_2^0 \dfrac{dx_2^0}{dt}}{r_0} = U \frac{x_1^0}{r_0} \qquad (4.21)$$

From the last two equations we have

$$\frac{dr_0}{dx_2^0} = -\frac{r_0}{\gamma} \qquad (4.22)$$

whence

$$r_0 = R_0 \exp(-x_2^0/\gamma) \qquad (4.23)$$

with an appropriate constant R_0.

These relations enable us to describe the path of the free vortex.

As x_2^0 approaches negative infinity the distance r_0 increases indefinitely and exponentially with respect to x_2^0 so that since $r_0 = \sqrt{(x_1^0)^2 + (x_2^0)^2}$ we have approximately

$$|x_1^0| = R_0 \exp(-x_2^0/\gamma)$$

If $R_0^2 > \gamma^2/e^2$ the curve breaks up into separate parts. If $R_0^2 < \gamma^2/e^2$ this does not happen. This can be easily seen by examining the condition that the transcendental equation

$$(x_2^0)^2 = R_0^2 \exp(-2x_2^0/\gamma)$$

has more than one root.

When x_2^0 is positive and increases, r_0 and x_1^0 decreases; hence r_0 reaches a minimum when x_1^0 reaches zero. This occurs when

$$x_2^0 = R_0 \exp(-x_2^0/\gamma); \qquad (4.24)$$

starting from the point where this happens x_1^0 increases and x_2^0 decreases as t increases. The free vortex thus moves away from the airfoil.

The condition $R_0^2 < \gamma^2/e^2$ will be satisfied in an actual case since in an actual flow the free vortex will start its motion from a point very near the trailing edge of the airfoil. The most important feature is the downward movement of the free vortex, for dx_2^0/dt is always negative.

According to formula (4.7) the force exerted by the fluid on the airfoil is given by

$$H = i\rho\Gamma\left[U + \frac{1}{2\pi i}\frac{1}{\bar{z}^0(t)}\right] \tag{4.25}$$

or

$$F_1 = \rho\gamma U^2 x_1^0(t)r_0^{-2}(t) \tag{4.26}$$

and

$$F_2 = \rho\Gamma U + \rho\gamma U x_2^0(t)r_0^{-2}(t) \tag{4.27}$$

We see that the lift is diminished when $x_2^0(t) < 0$. More important is the presence of a positive component F_1 in the direction of the flow at infinity. This component is called the "drag". It represents the effect of the process of accelerating the fluid to its final velocity. Obviously this drag approaches zero as time goes on. After a considerable time we have approximately

$$x_1^0 = Ut \tag{4.28}$$

since $x_1^0 \sim r_0$ and thus $r_0 \sim Ut$ whence from (4.23)

$$|x_2^0| = \gamma\log\frac{Ut}{R_0} \tag{4.29}$$

Accordingly

$$F_1 = \rho\gamma\,\frac{U}{t} \tag{4.30}$$

$$F_2 = \rho\Gamma U - \rho\gamma U^{-1} t^{-2}\log\frac{Ut}{R_0} \tag{4.31}$$

In a later section we shall give a more refined approximate treatment of the problem of accelerating the flow to its final velocity.

CHAPTER 5

Vortex Sheets

In the previous two chapters we considered flows in which the vorticity is concentrated on lines. In this section we proceed to discuss flows in which the vorticity is concentrated on surfaces. Such surfaces are called vortex sheets.

First we consider quite generally discontinuity surfaces, i.e. surfaces across which the flow quantities suffer discontinuities. It is assumed though, that these quantities approach definite values when the surface is approached from either side. Thus the discontinuities are assumed to be jumps. By n we denote the unit normal vector at each point of the surface, directed toward a particular side, called the positive side. The limits of a flow quantity q on approaching the positive or negative side will be denoted by q^+ and q^- respectively. The jump of q will be denoted by $\hat{q}$ and not by $[q]$ as usual i.e.

$$\hat{q} = q^+ - q^- \tag{5.1}$$

Of particular interest is the jump of the velocity $\hat{u}$. The vector

$$\gamma = [n, \hat{u}] \tag{5.2}$$

which is evidently tangential to the surface will play a particular role in the following. To clarify this role we consider a directed segment $\mathscr{A}$ on a surface $\mathscr{F}$ and let s be the arc length along it; further we denote by τ the unit vector perpendicular to $\mathscr{A}$ and tangential to $\mathscr{F}$ so directed that $\mathscr{A}, \tau, n$ form a right hand system. Then we consider the circulation $C_\mathscr{C}$ of the flow over a circuit $\mathscr{C}$ which runs first close to $\mathscr{A}$ on the positive side and then close to $\mathscr{A}$ on the negative side but in opposite directions. Finally we determine the limit that this circulation approaches when we let the circuit $\mathscr{C}$ shrink to the segment $\mathscr{A}$ run through in positive direction on the positive side and in negative

33

direction on the negative side. We may also say that $\mathscr{C}$ approaches the circuit $\mathscr{A}^+ - \mathscr{A}^-$. The limit of $C_{\mathscr{C}}$ will be denoted by $C_{\mathscr{A}^+ - \mathscr{A}^-}$.

In order to determine this limit we need only observe that the component of the velocity u in direction of the segment $\mathscr{A}$ can be given by

$$(u[\tau, n])$$

whence

$$C_{\mathscr{A}^+ - \mathscr{A}^-} = \int_{\mathscr{A}} (u^+[\tau, n]) \, ds - \int_{\mathscr{A}} (u^-[\tau, n]) \, ds = \int_{\mathscr{A}} (\hat{u}[\tau, n]) \, ds$$

Now by (5.2),

$$(\hat{u}[\tau, n]) = (\tau[n, \hat{u}]) = (\tau\gamma)$$

hence

$$C_{\mathscr{A}^+ - \mathscr{A}^-} = \int_{\mathscr{A}} (\tau\gamma) \, ds \tag{5.3}$$

It is therefore justified to call the term $(\tau\gamma)$ the "circulation per unit length" around the vector τ and, since $(\tau\gamma)$ is the component of γ in the direction of τ, we may call γ the "vector of circulation per unit length".

Not every discontinuity surface will be called a vortex sheet. The first requirement we stipulate is that no fluid be generated or destroyed at the surface. In other words we require that the flux of mass through the surface is the same on both sides,

$$(u^+ n) = (u^- n) \tag{5.4}$$

When this condition is placed in the form

$$(\hat{u} n) = 0 \tag{5.5}$$

it states that the jump of velocity should be tangential to the surface.

The requirements to be imposed next involve the motion of the surface $\mathscr{F}$. We may speak of the motion of each point of $\mathscr{F}$ only if points of $\mathscr{F}$ at one time can be identified with a definite point of $\mathscr{F}$ at a different time. This will be possible for a *bound vortex sheet* which is the idealization of a shell consisting of solid matter but not for a *free sheet*, which is the idealization of a thin layer of fluid in which the vorticity is large.

We first consider a bound vortex sheet. Such a sheet is defined by the condition that *no fluid crosses it*. Denoting by U the velocity of each point of the sheet we may express the flux of mass into and out of the sheet by $(\{u^+ - U\}n)$ and $(\{u^- - U\}n)$ respectively. The condition that no fluid crosses the sheet can therefore be expressed in the form

$$(\{u^+ - U\}n) = (\{u^- - U\}n) = 0$$

or

I $$(u^+n) = (u^-n) = (Un) \tag{5.6}$$

which states that the flux of mass through the sheet vanishes when it is observed from a frame which has the velocity of the sheet at the point and the time considered.

Next we consider the flux of momentum across the sheet. The momentum entering the sheet at the negative side per unit time is $\rho u^-(\{u^- - U\}n)$ and the momentum leaving the sheet at positive side per unit time is $\rho u^+(\{u^+ - U\}n)$. The balance, the total momentum flux across the surface, can be given as

$$\rho \hat{u}(\{u^+ - U\}n) = \rho \hat{u}(\{u^- - U\}n) \tag{5.7}$$

as seen from (5.4). Condition (5.6) now entails that the total momentum flux across the bound sheet vanishes. As a consequence of this fact the force per unit area exerted by the fluid on the sheet is the force per unit area exerted by the sheet on the fluid balance since otherwise these forces together would create momentum which would have to be transported out of the sheet. The force per unit area F exerted by the fluid results solely from the pressure p; it is therefore

$$F = -\hat{p}n$$

For a *free sheet* the velocity of each of its points cannot be defined in a strict sense; for, the fluid particles on the upper and the lower side move differently and therefore it is impossible to associate each point of the sheet with a definite particle.

Suppose we identify the points of the sheet at different times in an arbitrary fashion and thus artificially define the velocity U of each point of the sheet. Then we notice that only the tangential component of this velocity is affected by this arbitrariness while the normal component (Un) is independent of it. Only this normal component enters the expressions $(\{u^+ - U\}n)$ and $(\{u^- - U\}n)$ for the mass flux into and out of the sheet. These expressions are therefore valid also for a free sheet. The same is true of formula (5.7) for the momentum flux.

Since the free sheet cannot sustain any force a momentum flux could solely be created by the resultant pressure, i.e.

$$-\hat{p}n = \rho\hat{u}(\{u^+ - U\}n) = \rho\hat{u}(\{u^- - U\}n) \qquad (5.8)$$

The vector on the left hand side here has normal direction while the vector on the right hand side has tangential direction since $\hat{u}$ is tangential by (5.5). Consequently, each side vanishes. We assume that $\mathscr{F}$ is really a vortex sheet and that hence the vector of circulation per unit length γ does not vanish on $\mathscr{F}$, or what is equivalent by (5.2) that $\hat{u}$ does not vanish on $\mathscr{F}$. From the vanishing of the right members of (5.8) we then conclude that the relation

I $$(u^+n) = (u^-n) = (Un)$$

holds.

This is the same relation (5.8) that was required for bound sheets. *The condition that no fluid crosses the sheet is thus seen to hold for free as well as for bound vortex sheets.* A sheet which satisfies this condition will be called "proper".

The vanishing of the left member of relation (5.8) leads to the condition

II $$\hat{p} = 0 \qquad (5.9)$$

that *the pressure is the same on both sides of a free sheet.*

It was explained above that only the normal component of the velocity of a point of a free vortex sheet is intrinsically defined and that the tangential component could be chosen arbitrarily. Nevertheless, there is a particular choice of the tangential component which has great advantages and which therefore will be adopted.

We first introduce the *mean value of velocities* on both sides of the sheet

$$\tilde{u} = \tfrac{1}{2}(u^+ + u^-) \qquad (5.10)$$

and then adopt

$$U = \tilde{u} \qquad (5.11)$$

as the velocity of any point of the free sheet. Evidently, the normal component of this velocity satisfies condition I, see (5.6), because of (5.4). We proceed to show that this choice of the sheet velocity entails analogues of the two basic vortex theorems which were formulated at the end of chapter 2.

First of all we note that points of the vortex sheet at different times are now identified. Let σ_1, σ_2 be two parameters characterizing points $x = x(\sigma_1, \sigma_2)$ of the sheet at an initial time $t = 0$, the "same" point $x = x(\sigma_1, \sigma_2, t)$ at a different time is given by the solution of the differential equation

$$\frac{d}{dt} x(\sigma_1, \sigma_2, t) = \tilde{u}(x(\sigma_1, \sigma_2, t), t)$$

for which $x(\sigma_1, \sigma_2, 0) = x(\sigma_1, \sigma_2)$. For any quantity $q(x, t)$ depending on the flow quantities we can introduce the "material derivative"

$$\frac{dq}{dt} = \frac{d}{dt} q(x(\sigma_1, \sigma_2, t), t) \tag{5.12}$$

Clearly, whenever the point $x = x(\sigma_1, \sigma_2, t)$ lies on the sheet we have

$$\frac{dq}{dt} = \nabla_t q(x, t) + (\tilde{u}\nabla)q(x, t) \tag{5.13}$$

If, instead of q, the jump of a quantity is taken we write

$$\frac{d\hat{q}}{dt} = \nabla_t \hat{q}(x, t) + (\tilde{u}\nabla)\hat{q}(x, t)$$

although we should properly have taken the jump $\nabla\hat{q}$ of ∇q and accordingly have written $\widehat{(\tilde{u}\nabla)q}$ instead of $(\tilde{u}\nabla)\hat{q}$. Similarly we write $\nabla\tilde{q}$ instead of the mean value of $\widetilde{\nabla q}$ of ∇q.

We now derive a basic formula for the flow quantities on the sheet by taking the jump of the basic equation

$$\nabla_t u + (u\nabla)u + \rho^{-1}\nabla p = 0$$

see (1.10). We note that the jump of a product $q_1 q_2$ can be written as

$$\widehat{q_1 q_2} = \hat{q}_1 \tilde{q}_2 + \tilde{q}_1 \hat{q}_2$$

The jump of $(u\nabla)u$ can, therefore, be written as

$$(\hat{u}\nabla)\tilde{u} + (\tilde{u}\nabla)\hat{u}$$

although properly we should write

$$(\widehat{u\nabla})\tilde{u} + (\tilde{u}\widehat{\nabla})u$$

Thus we obtain the relation

$$\nabla_t \hat{u} + (\tilde{u}\nabla)\hat{u} + (\hat{u}\nabla)\tilde{u} = -\rho^{-1}\widehat{\nabla p}$$

or $$\frac{d\hat{u}}{dt} = -(\hat{u}\nabla)\tilde{u} - \rho^{-1}\widehat{\nabla p} \qquad (5.14)$$

We now consider a segment $\mathscr{A} = \mathscr{A}(t)$ on the free sheet which is attached to the sheet so as if each point moved with the velocity $\tilde{u}$. Letting $x = x(\sigma, t), \sigma_1 \leqq \sigma \leqq \sigma_2$, be a parametric representation of this arc, the relation

$$\nabla_t x(\sigma, t) = \tilde{u}(x(\sigma, t), t)$$

should hold. We then state the two theorems which hold for free sheets provided the flow is irrotational on both sides.

Theorem I. The circulation $C_{\mathscr{A}(t)}$ of the segment $\mathscr{A}(t)$ remains constant.

Theorem II. The segment $\mathscr{A}(t)$ remains a vortex line if it once was a vortex line.

We shall first prove Theorem II. Setting $y = \nabla_\sigma x(\sigma, t)$ we may express the condition that $\mathscr{A}$ is a vortex line by the requirement $(\hat{u}y) = 0$ instead of requiring that the vector of circulation per unit length γ be parallel to y and thus tangential to the arc $\mathscr{A}$. We calculate the material derivative of the quantity

$$(\hat{u}y)$$

Since

$$\frac{dy}{dt} = \nabla_t \nabla_\sigma x(\sigma, t) = \nabla_\sigma \nabla_t x(\sigma, t) = \nabla_\sigma \tilde{u} = (y\nabla)\tilde{u}$$

we find

$$\frac{d}{dt}(\hat{u}y) = \hat{u}(y\nabla)\tilde{u} + y\frac{d}{dt}\hat{u}$$

Now we use formula (5.14) and observe that the relation $\hat{p} = 0$, cf. (5.9), implies the relation

$$(y\nabla\hat{p}) = 0$$

Hence we obtain

$$\frac{d}{dt}(\hat{u}y) = \hat{u}(y\nabla)\tilde{u} - y(\hat{u}\nabla)\tilde{u}$$

If ∇ were a proper vector this expression could by (1.2) be written in the form

$$\frac{d}{dt}(\hat{u}y) = ([y,\hat{u}][\nabla,\tilde{u}]) \tag{5.15}$$

This relation remains valid even for the differential operator ∇ since the order of the terms is so chosen that ∇ applies only on $\tilde{u}$ as it should. The vector $[\nabla,\tilde{u}]$ is the mean value of the curl $[\nabla,u]$. Since by assumption this curl vanishes on both sides of the sheet, the same is true of the mean value. Consequently,

$$\frac{d}{dt}(\hat{u}y) = 0 \tag{5.16}$$

We conclude that the term $(\hat{u}y)$ is zero for all times if it was zero once. Thus Theorem II is proved.

In order to prove Theorem I we start with the expression

$$C_{\mathscr{A}(t)} = \int_{\sigma_1}^{\sigma_2} (\hat{u}y)\,d\sigma$$

for $C_{\mathscr{A}(t)}$, which is equivalent with the expression (5.3). Relation (5.16) yields immediately

$$\frac{d}{dt}C_{\mathscr{A}(t)} = \int_{\sigma_1}^{\sigma_2} \frac{d}{dt}(\hat{u}y)\,d\sigma = 0$$

Thus Theorem I is proved.

It may be mentioned that the condition that the flow be irrotational on both sides could be weakened. Since both y and $\hat{u}$ are tangential, $[y,\hat{u}]$ is normal; hence only the normal component of $[\nabla,\tilde{u}]$ enters the right member of (5.15). Thus it is seen that it is sufficient to require that the normal component of $[\nabla,\tilde{u}]$ be zero on the sheet.

There is another approach to Theorem I in connection with formulas which will be important in later applications. We do not assume that the sheet is free but we assume that both sides of the sheet can be connected by paths that pass through a region in which the flow is irrotational. We then may introduce a potential $\phi(x,t)$ in this region and consider the jump $\hat{\phi}(x,t)$ at each point x of the sheet. We denote by $\mathscr{B}_x(t)$ a path which connects the point x on the lower side of $\mathscr{F}$ with the point on the upper side; the circulation $C_x(t) = C_{\mathcal{B}_x}(t)$ of this path is then just equal to the jump in potential

$$\hat{\phi}(x, t) = C_x(t) \tag{5.17}$$

We now take the jump of Bernoulli's equation

$$\rho \nabla_t \phi + \frac{\rho}{2} |u|^2 + p = 0$$

cf. (2.7). Since the jump of $|u|^2 = (uu)$ can be written as $2(\hat{u}\tilde{u})$ we obtain the relation

$$\rho \nabla_t \hat{\phi} + \rho(\tilde{u}\hat{u}) + \hat{p} = 0 \tag{5.18}$$

Since, evidently, $\hat{u} = \nabla \hat{\phi}$, we may write this equation in the form

$$\rho \frac{d}{dt} \hat{\phi} + \hat{p} = 0 \tag{5.19}$$

or by (5.17)

$$\hat{p}(x, t) = -\rho \frac{d}{dt} C_x(t) \tag{5.20}$$

For a free sheet on which $\hat{p} = 0$, relation (5.18) implies the important relation

$$\frac{d}{dt} \hat{\phi}(x, t) = 0 \tag{5.21}$$

or, what is equivalent, $C_x(t) = $ constant.

For steady flow, relation (5.18) assumes the form

$$\hat{p} = -\rho(\tilde{u}\hat{u}) \tag{5.22}$$

which can be brought into the form

$$\hat{p}n = -\rho[\tilde{u} - (\tilde{u}n)n, \gamma]; \tag{5.23}$$

this may be considered an analogue to the Kutta-Joukowski formula, the tangential component $\tilde{u} - (\tilde{u}n)n$ of $\tilde{u}$ taking the part of the velocity at infinity.

Interesting consequences can be drawn from relation (5.21) for free sheets. Consider two vortex lines $\mathscr{V}_1$ and $\mathscr{V}_2$. The circulation of an arc $\mathscr{A}$ connecting any two points of these lines is, of course, independent of the choice of these points. This circulation is different from zero if the two lines $\mathscr{V}_1$ and $\mathscr{V}_2$ are sufficiently close together since otherwise there would be no discontinuity of u on the sheet. Suppose now the two lines $\mathscr{V}_1, \mathscr{V}_2$ ended at an edge of the sheet at two points $\mathscr{P}_1, \mathscr{P}_2$. Then the circulation of the arc $\mathscr{A}_{12}$ connecting these two points along the edge would be different from zero when this arc is approached on the sheet while it would be zero when approached from the outside. Thus a contradiction would ensue unless the flow had an appropriate singularity at the edge. The appropriate singularity is that of a vortex filament with a non-constant circulation. Let C_1 and C_2 be the circulations around the filament at the points $\mathscr{P}_1$ and $\mathscr{P}_2$; then the circulation $C_{\mathscr{A}_{12}}$ along the segment $\mathscr{A}_{12}$ when approached on the sheet must be

$$C_{\mathscr{A}_{12}} = C_2 - C_1$$

Flows involving a vortex filament with non-constant circulation attached to the edge of a vortex sheet will play a major role in the theory of airfoils of finite span.

If no vortex filament is attached to one of the edges of the sheet no vortex line on the sheet can end at that edge.

In the subsequent treatment of vortex sheets we shall use approximation methods. It seems that up to now no flow involving a vortex sheet has been given exactly, with one exception. The exception is the two-dimensional steady flow around a plane strip $|x_1| < a, x_2 = 0$. The complex potential of this flow as a function of $z = x_1 + ix_2$ is

$$\chi = \pm U_2 \sqrt{(a^2 - x^2)} \quad \text{for } x_2 \gtrless 0$$

One observes that this function is continuous for $x_2 = 0$ when $|x_1| \geqq a$, but it is discontinuous on the slit $x_2 = 0, |x_1| < a$. The jump of χ there given by

$$\hat{\chi} = \hat{\phi} = 2U_2 \sqrt{(a^2 - x_1^2)}$$

is real. The complex velocity of the flow is

$$\bar{w} = \frac{d\chi}{dz} = \mp U_2 z / \sqrt{(a^2 - z^2)}, \quad x_2 \gtrless 0$$

as z approaches infinity $\bar{w}$ approaches the value $-iU_2$ so that $u \to \{0, U_2\}$ as $z \to \infty$. At the slit we find

$$u_1 = \mp U_2 x_1 / \sqrt{(a^2 - x_1^2)}, \quad u_2 = 0, \quad x_2 \gtrless 0$$

whence

$$\hat{u}_1 = -2U_2 x_1 / \sqrt{(a^2 - x^2)}, \quad \hat{u}_2 = 0, \quad \tilde{u}_1 = \tilde{u}_2 = 0$$

Since the velocity $\tilde{u}$ of the slit vanishes it can be maintained in steady flow. The vorticity vector on the sheet is

$$\gamma = -\frac{2x_1}{\sqrt{(a^2 - x_1^2)}}\{0, 0, 1\}$$

The vortex lines, $x_1 = $ const., $x_2 = 0$ do not end at the edge $|x_1| = a$. The circulation C_x of a circuit connecting the lower point x_1 with the upper point x_1

$$C_x = \hat{\phi}(x_1) = 2U_2 \sqrt{(a^2 - x_1^2)}$$

vanishes at the end points.

CHAPTER 6

Airfoil with Trailing Vortex Sheet

Vortex sheets develop at the trailing edges of airfoils with non-constant profiles or moving with non-constant velocity.

In order to see why this should happen let us consider the steady motion of an airfoil that started from rest. From the theory of airfoils of infinite span with constant profile we know that—due to the action of viscosity—the flow past the airfoil adjusts itself in such a way that the flow velocity at the trailing edge is finite. This condition, introduced by Kutta and Joukowski, will be referred to as the "Kutta condition" as is customary. We also know that during the process of adjustment the flow acquires an appropriate circulation. After this circulation has built up, the action of the viscosity can be disregarded. Naturally one is inclined to assume that the Kutta condition should also be satisfied if the airfoil is not of infinite span or, more generally, if it does not have a constant profile. The circulation that is needed to satisfy the Kutta condition, however, is not constant along such an airfoil. Therefore, the flow outside the airfoil cannot be purely irrotational.

The assumption is made, apparently in very good approximation, that the vorticity needed to balance the change of circulation along the airfoil is concentrated in a vortex sheet which is attached to the trailing edge. As a matter of fact, every non steady flow can be described in a similar manner. Assuming that the Kutta condition is satisfied the circulation will vary in time. The vorticity for the balance is again concentrated in a vortex sheet which leaves the trailing edge. This is the case even if the airfoil is of infinite span with a constant profile so that the flow is two-dimensional.

We proceed to formulate the conditions to be satisfied by a flow past an airfoil combined with a vortex sheet. Later on we shall discuss approximate methods by which the problems can be treated explicitly.

43

We let the airfoil be bounded by two curves

$$x_2 = y^{\pm}(x_1, x_3, t), \tag{6.1}$$

described with the aid of two "profile functions" $y^{\pm}(x_1, x_3, t)$. We assume

$$y^{-}(x_1, x_3, t) \leqq y^{+}(x_1, x_3, t) \tag{6.2}$$

thus the superscripts $^+$ and $^-$ characterize the upper and lower side respectively.

The independent variable x_1 will be restricted to an interval

$$x_1^{+}(x_3, t) \geqq x_1 \geqq x_1^{-}(x_3, t) \tag{6.3}$$

so that $x_1^{+}(x_3, t) - x_1^{-}(x_3, t)$ is the "depth" of the profile. This depth may depend on the variable x_3; if it is positive only in a finite interval

$$x_3^{-} < x_3 < x_3^{+} \tag{6.4}$$

we say that the airfoil has a finite span of length $x_3^{+} - x_3^{-}$, see Fig. 6.1.

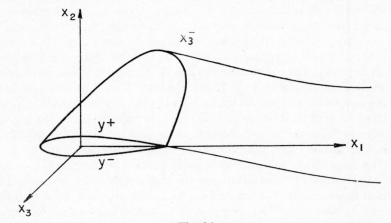

Fig. 6.1.

Except for the vortex sheet the airflow is irrotational and can, therefore, be described by a potential $\phi = \phi(x, t)$. The velocity is then given by

$$u = \nabla\phi \tag{6.5}$$

We proceed to formulate the condition that the air slide along the profile, i.e. the condition that the difference of the flow velocity at a point of the profile and the velocity of that point is tangential to the profile. It does not matter for this purpose how the points of the profile at different times are identified with each other. We may just as well assume that the points with the same coordinates x_1, x_3 remain the same. Accordingly, the velocity of the point of the airfoil is

$$\nabla_t \{x_1, y^\pm(x_1, x_3, t), x_3\} = \{0, \nabla_t y^\pm, 0\} \tag{6.6}$$

The velocity of the actual motion of this point as a material particle can differ from this velocity only by a tangential vector. The difference of flow and airfoil velocity

$$\{u_1^\pm, u_2^\pm - \nabla_t y^\pm, u_3^\pm\} \tag{6.7}$$

should be perpendicular to the normal to the airfoil, which is evidently parallel to the vector

$$\{\nabla_1 y^\pm, -1, \nabla_3 y^\pm\} \tag{6.8}$$

Hence the *condition of sliding* is

$$u_2^\pm = \nabla_1 y^\pm \cdot u_1^\pm + \nabla_3 y^\pm \cdot u_3^\pm + \nabla_t y^\pm$$

at $$x_2 = y^\pm(x_1, x_3, t)$$

of course, $u^\pm$ is the flow velocity at the upper and lower surface respectively.

The *vortex sheet* can be described by the function

$$x_2 = y(x_1, x_3, t), \quad x_1^+(x_3, t) \leqq x_1 \tag{6.9}$$

The condition of sliding is also to be imposed, that is

I $$u_2^\pm = \nabla_1 y \cdot u_1^\pm + \nabla_3 y \cdot u_3^\pm + \nabla_t y$$

Because of the free character of the sheet the additional condition

II $$\nabla_t \hat{\phi} + \tilde{u}\hat{u} = 0$$

is to be imposed [cf. (5.18), (5.9)]. We take the attitude that the functions

$$y^\pm(x_1, x_3, t)$$

describing the moving profile, are given while the function $y(x_1, x_3, t)$ describing the vortex sheet is to be found. Of course, the Kutta condition must be used.

CHAPTER 7

Flat Airfoils

The approximation method to be described is based on two assumptions:

1. The two sides of the airfoil differ little from the two sides of a section of the plane $x_2 = 0$, the "base" of the airfoil.

2. The motion of each point of the airfoil differs little from a certain motion of a point in the plane $x_2 = 0$, the "main motion" of the airfoil.

We shall temporarily change our notations. The points in space will be denoted by $X = \{X_1, X_2, X_3\}$; the two sides of the airfoil by $X_2 = Y^{\pm}(X_1, X_3, t)$. The velocity potential will be denoted by $\Phi = \Phi(X, t)$. The main motion of the airfoil will be denoted by

$$X = X^a(t) \quad \text{with} \quad X_2^a(t) = 0 \tag{7.1}$$

$$U^a = \nabla_t X^a(t) \tag{7.2}$$

Since we intend to describe the resulting flow with reference to the main motion we introduce the "adjusted position"

$$x = X - X^a(t) \tag{7.3}$$

as now variable; furthermore we introduce the "adjusted" profile function $y^{\pm}(x_1, x_3, t)$ by

$$y^{\pm}(x_1, x_3, t) = Y^{\pm}(X_1^a(t) + x_1, X_3^a(t) + x_3, t) \tag{7.4}$$

Also we introduce the "adjusted" potential

$$\phi(x, t) = \Phi(X^a(t) + x, t) \tag{7.5}$$

Evidently

$$u = \nabla\phi = \nabla\Phi = U \tag{7.6}$$

Since, as is easily seen,

$$\nabla_t Y = \nabla_t y - \nabla_1 y \cdot U_1^a - \nabla_3 y \cdot U_3^a \tag{7.7}$$

condition I of chapter 6 becomes

I' $\qquad u_2^{\pm} = \nabla_1 y^{\pm} \cdot (u_1^{\pm} - U_1^a) + \nabla_3 y^{\pm} \cdot (u_3^{\pm} - U_3^a) + \nabla_t y^{\pm}$

Because of

$$\nabla_t \Phi = \nabla_t \phi - (u \, U^a) \qquad (7.8)$$

Bernoulli's law attains the form

$$\nabla_t \phi - (u \, U^a) + \tfrac{1}{2} |u|^2 + \rho^{-1} p = \text{const.} \qquad (7.9)$$

Condition II on the free vortex sheet, therefore, finally becomes

II' $\qquad \nabla_t \hat{\phi} + (\tilde{u} - U^a)\hat{u} = 0$

Sometimes it is opportune to describe the flow with reference to an observer who moves with the velocity $U^a(t)$. For this observer the fluid has at infinity the velocity

$$U^{\infty}(t) = -U^a(t) \qquad (7.10)$$

Also x is the position as it would appear for this observer and $u + U^{\infty}$ is the flow velocity relative to this observer. In the following we shall use U^{∞} instead of U^a.

Before we can apply the approximation procedure we must assume that a manifold of profiles is given which depend on a parameter ε such that the adjusted profile functions admit an *expansion*

$$y(x_1, x_3, t) = \varepsilon y^{(1)}(x_1, x_3, t) + \varepsilon^2 y^{(2)}(x_1, x_3, t) + \dots \qquad (7.11)$$

We assume that the adjusted profile function of the vortex sheet admits an expansion of the same form. Further we assume that the adjusted velocity potential and velocity as functions of (x, t) admit expansions of the form

$$u(x, t) = \varepsilon u^{(1)}(x, t) + \varepsilon^2 u^{(2)}(x, t) + \dots \qquad (7.12)$$

$$\phi(x, t) = \varepsilon \phi^{(1)}(x, t) + \varepsilon^2 \phi^{(2)}(x, t) + \dots \qquad (7.13)$$

The function $\phi^{(1)}(x, t)$ is evidently also a potential function.

Before we can expand conditions I' and II' with respect to ε we must insert $x_2 = \varepsilon y^{\pm}(x_1, x_3, t) + \dots$ in the arguments of u and $\nabla_t \phi$. Condition I' then becomes

I'' $\quad \varepsilon u_2^{\pm}(x_1, 0, x_3, t) = \varepsilon U_1^{\infty}(t) \nabla_1 y^{\pm (1)}(x_1, x_3, t)$

$\qquad + \varepsilon U_3^{\infty}(t) \nabla_3 y^{\pm (1)}(x_1, x_3, t) + \varepsilon \nabla_t y^{\pm (1)}(x_1, x_3, t) + \dots$

omitting terms of higher order in ε; condition II' becomes

II'' $\qquad \varepsilon \nabla_t \hat{\phi}^{(1)}(x_1, 0, x_3, t) + \varepsilon U^{\infty}(t) \hat{u}(x_1, 0, x_3, t) + ... = 0$

We see that these conditions are written in a form in which they are to be satisfied at the *bases* of profile and sheet, i.e. on the projections of them on the (x_1, x_3)-plane. The fact that in the original form these conditions are to be satisfied at the sheets will affect the terms of higher order in ε.

In the following we are satisfied with terms of first order in ε. It is convenient to write y, ϕ, u instead of $\varepsilon y^{(1)}, \varepsilon \phi^{(1)}, \varepsilon u^{(1)}$. The terms of first order of condition I'' and II'' then assume the form

I° $\qquad u_2^{\pm}(x, t) = U_1^{\infty}(t) \nabla_1 y^{\pm}(x_1, x_3, t) + U_3^{\infty}(t) \nabla_3 y^{\pm}(x_1, x_3, t)$

$$+ \nabla_t y^{\pm}(x_1, x_3, t)$$

$\qquad$ for $\quad x_2 = 0, \qquad x_1^-(t) \leqq x_1$

II° $\qquad \nabla_t \hat{\phi}(x, t) + U^{\infty}(t) \hat{u}(x, t) = 0$

$\qquad$ for $\quad x_2 = 0, \qquad x_1^+(t) \leqq x_1$

Condition I° as given here holds for the airfoil and for the vortex sheet. This condition can be split into two parts by taking the average and the jump of the conditions on both sides. The resulting forms are of particular interest on the sheet.

$\tilde{I}_{sh}^{\circ}$ $\qquad\qquad \tilde{u}_2 = U_1^{\infty} \nabla_1 \tilde{y} + U_3^{\infty} \nabla_3 \tilde{y} + \nabla_t \tilde{y}$

$\qquad$ for $\quad x_2 = 0, \qquad x_1^+(t) \leqq x_1$

and

$\hat{I}_{sh}^{\circ}$ $\qquad\qquad \hat{u}_2 = 0 \quad$ for $\quad x_2 = 0, \qquad x_1^+(t) \leqq x_1$

From condition $\hat{I}_{sh}^{\circ}$ we see that the vertical velocity is continuous on the sheet or rather on the base of the sheet.

The flow satisfying conditions I° and II° will be called the "first order" flow.

It is important to note that the conditions I° do not exclude that in the first order flow fluid crosses the base of the airfoil or of the sheet. These bases are, therefore, not proper vortex sheets themselves. The manner in which the first order flow may still serve to describe approximately a flow around the airfoil with a proper trailing vortex sheet will be shown in connection with the examples.

Condition II° can also be put in the form

$$\frac{d}{dt}\hat{\Phi}(X,t) = 0 \qquad \text{on} \quad X_2 = 0, \qquad X_1 \geqq X_1^+(t) \qquad (7.14)$$

or $\qquad \hat{\Phi}(X,t) = \text{const.} \qquad \text{on} \quad X_2 = 0, \qquad X_1 \geqq X_1^+(t) \qquad (7.15)$

In words, the jump in potential at a fixed point X does not change in time after it has been created. The time of creation is, of course, the time when the trailing edge $X_1 = X_1^+(t)$ passes through the point X. Note that the jump $\hat{\Phi}$ is the circulation of a circuit connecting the lower point X^- with the upper point X^+ on the base of the sheet. It is clear that this should be so; for, the circulation of a material circuit does not change in time and the flow velocity is zero in lowest order.

In terms of the variable x, instead of X, condition (7.15) can be put in the form

$$\hat{\Phi}(X + X^\infty(t), t) = \text{const.} \qquad (7.16)$$

where $X^\infty(t) = -X^a(t)$ represents the motion of the fluid at infinity when observed by the observer who moves with the airfoil. Thus one can say that the circulation $\hat{\phi}$, created at the trailing edge and shed into the fluid, is transported with the velocity $dX^\infty/dt = U^\infty$.

The procedure in determining the first order flow is the following. One should find the potential function $\phi(x,t)$ which assumes the normal derivatives $u_2^\pm$ given by I° at both sides of the base of the profile and for which the jump of the normal derivative $\hat{u}_2$ is given on the sheet.

CHAPTER 8

Stationary Airfoil of Infinite Span

The approximation method which has been described is applicable even to the problem of finding the flow past an airfoil of infinite span with constant profile moving with constant velocity, although this problem could also be solved by conformal mapping. The absence of a vortex sheet in this flow, of course, is irrelevant. Since the flow is two-dimensional, we assume that all quantities depend only on x_1, x_2 and not on x_3. Since the airfoil moves with constant velocity, the problem may be transformed into that of a steady flow with a velocity $U^\infty = \{U_1^\infty, 0\}$ at infinity; the flow need only be observed by an observer moving with velocity $U^a = -U^\infty$.

We assume the coordinate system so chosen that the base of the profile is the segment $-a \leqq x_1 \leqq a$ of the x_1-axis. The two given profile functions $y^\pm(x_1)$ are then defined in this interval; of course, they are independent of the time. The condition of sliding along the profile assumes the form

I $$u_2^\pm = U_1^\infty \nabla_1 y^\pm \qquad \text{on } x_2 = 0, \qquad -a \leqq x_1 \leqq a$$

We then seek the potential flow satisfying this condition together with

$$u \to U = \{U_1^\infty, 0\} \qquad \text{as } x_1^2 + x_2^2 \to \infty \tag{8.1}$$

and the Kutta condition at $x_1 = 1, x_2 = 0$.

In order to find this flow we introduce the independent variable $z = x_1 + ix_2$ and the complex velocity potential

$$\chi = \phi + i\psi \tag{8.2}$$

for the flow in excess of the parallel flow. The complex potential of the full flow is then

$$U_1 z + \chi \tag{8.3}$$

We recall that the velocity components are given by

$$\nabla_1 \phi = \nabla_2 \psi = u_1 + U_1^\infty \tag{8.4}$$

$$\nabla_2 \phi = -\nabla_1 \psi = u_2 \tag{8.5}$$

We may satisfy condition I by simply prescribing the stream function along the profile

$$\psi(x_1, \pm 0) = -U_1^\infty y^\pm(x_1), \qquad -a \leqq x_1 \leqq a$$

In order to solve the problem we map the exterior of the slit $|x_1| \leqq a, x_2 = 0$ on the exterior of the unit circle $|\zeta| \geqq 1$ in a ζ-plane. The mapping is given by

$$z = \frac{a}{2}(\zeta + \zeta^{-1}) \tag{8.6}$$

We introduce polar coordinates ρ, θ by

$$\zeta = \rho\, e^{i\theta} \tag{8.7}$$

Since $\zeta = e^{i\theta}$ on the unit circle the slit is described by

$$z = \cos\theta \qquad |\theta| \leqq \pi \tag{8.8}$$

the upper and lower sides correspond to $\theta > 0$ and $\theta < 0$ respectively.

The boundary condition I for the complex potential function $\chi = \phi + i\psi$ can therefore be formulated as

$$\psi = -U_1^\infty y^\pm(\cos\theta) \qquad \theta \gtrless 0 \tag{8.9}$$

This can be seen upon substitution from equation (8.5) in I getting

$$-\nabla_1 \psi^\pm = U_1^\infty \nabla_1 y^\pm \tag{8.10}$$

relation (8.9) then follows upon integration of (8.10) and noticing that the complex velocity potential is determined up to an additive constant.

In characterizing the behavior of χ at infinity we should take account of the circulation of the flow which is to be determined. Denoting the counter circulation by Γ we state that the function

$$\chi - \frac{i\Gamma}{2\pi}\log\zeta \tag{8.11}$$

should die out as $|\zeta| \to \infty$ and hence be regular at infinity. On the unit circle the imaginary part ψ of this regular function has the same boundary values as ψ itself. The potential function

$$\psi - \frac{\Gamma}{2\pi}\log\rho \qquad (8.12)$$

could be given explicitly in terms of these boundary values with the aid of a well-known integral operation. Instead of doing this, we prefer to set up a power series expansion for the function

$$\chi - \frac{i\Gamma}{2\pi}\log\zeta \qquad (8.11)$$

$$\chi = \frac{i\Gamma}{2\pi}\log\zeta + \sum_{n=0}^{\infty} c_n \zeta^{-n} \qquad (8.13)$$

The coefficients c_n are to be determined so that the given boundary values of ψ possess the expansion

$$\psi = \operatorname{Im} \sum_{n=0}^{\infty} c_n e^{-in\theta} \qquad (8.14)$$

so that

$$U_1^\infty y^{\pm}(\cos\theta) = - \sum_{n=0}^{\infty} \operatorname{Im} c_n e^{-in\theta}, \qquad \theta \gtrless 0 \qquad (8.15)$$

It is thus seen that the coefficients can be obtained from the Fourier series expansion of the given function $y^{\pm}(\cos\theta)$. Assuming this expansion to be known we now may assume the coefficients c_n to be known.

We now shall satisfy the Kutta condition by determining the counter circulation Γ appropriately. We recall that the Kutta condition stated that the complex excess velocity $d\chi/dz$ be finite at the trailing edge. Clearly this means that

$$\frac{d\chi}{dz} = u_1 - iu_2 \qquad (8.16)$$

should be finite at $z = 1$. We may express this condition as a condition for the derivative

$$\frac{d\chi}{d\zeta} = \frac{d\chi}{dz} \cdot \frac{a}{2}\left(1 - \frac{1}{\zeta^2}\right)$$

3

Since the point $z = 1$ corresponds under the conformal mapping (8.6) to the point $\zeta = 1$, it is seen that condition (8.16) implies that

$$\frac{\partial \chi}{\partial \zeta} = 0 \qquad \text{at } \zeta = 1 \tag{8.17}$$

It could be shown that the latter condition is also sufficient to insure that (8.16) holds provided the profile functions $y^{\pm}(x_1)$ have continuous derivatives at $x_1 = 1$, which we assume.

Since the power series expansion of $d\chi/d\zeta$ is

$$\frac{d\chi}{d\zeta} = \frac{i\Gamma}{2\pi} \zeta^{-1} - \sum_{n=1}^{\infty} nc_n \zeta^{-n-1} \tag{8.18}$$

condition (8.17) assumes the form

$$\frac{i\Gamma}{2\pi} - \sum_{n=1}^{\infty} nc_n = 0 \tag{8.19}$$

The imaginary part of this equation yields the value of the counter circulation

$$\Gamma = 2\pi \sum_{n=1}^{\infty} n \operatorname{Im} c_n = 2\pi \sum_{n=1}^{\infty} nb_n \tag{8.20}$$

where b_n is the imaginary part of

$$c_n = a_n + ib_n \tag{8.21}$$

Thus the problem is solved in principle. The real part of the above relation vanishes automatically. We first note that this real part equals

$$\operatorname{Re} \frac{\partial \chi}{\partial \zeta} = \frac{\partial \psi}{\partial \eta} \tag{8.22}$$

where η is the imaginary part of $\zeta = \xi + i\eta$. Next we note that $\eta = \sin \theta$ along the unit circle $\zeta = e^{i\theta}$, hence

$$\frac{\partial \psi}{\partial \eta} = \frac{\partial \psi}{\partial \theta} \bigg/ \cos \theta = U_1^{\infty} \frac{dy^{\pm}(\cos \theta)}{d\cos \theta} \tan \theta \tag{8.23}$$

and this expression vanishes for $\theta = 0$.

CHAPTER 9

Unsteady Motion of an Airfoil of Infinite Span with a Constant Profile

If the velocity of the airfoil is not constant as in the problem discussed in the previous chapter, a vortex sheet develops from the trailing edge, see Fig. 9.1.

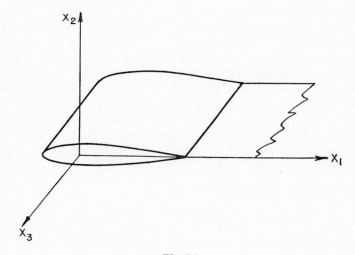

Fig. 9.1.

We assume that the motion of the airfoil differs little from a motion with the velocity $U^a(t) = \{U_1^a(t), 0\}$ in the negative x_1-direction. In other words, we assume that the airfoil at most executes small motions relative to the main motion. Accordingly, the airfoil will appear to be at rest except for small oscillations when observed by an observer moving with the main velocity $U^a(t)$. The profile functions $y^{\pm}(x_1)$ and the complex potential function $\chi = \phi + i\psi$ will depend on the time but do not depend on x_3. Accordingly, as follows from (I°, p. 49) upon integration with respect to x_1, the boundary conditions for this function can be brought into the form

$$\psi^\pm = -U_1^\infty(t)y^\pm(x_1,t) - \int_a^{x_1} \nabla_t y^\pm(x_1',t)dx_1', \quad |x_1| \leqq a, \quad x_2 = 0$$

(9.1)

after choosing a constant of integration appropriately; here we assume that the base of the airfoil falls on the segment $|x_1| \leqq a$. On the vortex sheet the condition

$$\psi = -U_1^\infty(t)y(x_1,t) - \int_{+a}^{x_1} \nabla_t y(x_1',t)dx_1', \quad x_1 \geqq a, \quad x_2 = 0 \quad (9.2)$$

is to be satisfied, as follows from (I°, p. 49). The function $y(x_1,t)$ in equation (9.2) is to be determined. Condition (9.2) implies that ψ is continuous on the base of the sheet.

Next we must express the condition that the circulation $\hat{\phi}$ is transported with the velocity $U_1^\infty(t)$. We know that in the approximation considered the circulation $\hat{\phi}$ at a point X at the base of the sheet does not change in time. If the relative position of this point is x, its absolute position is $X = x - X^\infty(t)$. Since $x_2 = 0$ on the base of the sheet and also $X_2^\infty(t) = 0$, we may introduce a function $g(\xi)$ such that

$$\hat{\phi}(x,t) = -g(x_1 - X_1^\infty(t)) \qquad (9.3)$$

It is clear that $g(\xi)$ is defined only for

$$\xi \geqq a - X_1^\infty(t) \qquad (9.3)_1$$

Assuming that the airfoil has been started in its motion at the time $t = 0$, we can define $g(\xi)$ only in the interval

$$a - X_1^\infty(0) \geqq \xi \geqq a - X_1^\infty(t) \qquad (9.3)_2$$

Incidentally, the time $t^+ = t^+(x_1,t)$ at which the circulation given by equation (9.3) was created, i.e. the time when the trailing edge passed through the point is defined by the condition

$$a - X_1^\infty(t^+) = x_1 - X_1^\infty(t) \qquad (9.4)$$

In order to solve the problem we split the function $\chi(x, t)$ into two parts

$$\chi(x, t) = \chi^p(x, t) + \chi^s(x, t) \tag{9.5}$$

The first contribution $\chi^p(x, t)$ corresponds to the flow around the airfoil without velocity at infinity and without circulation at infinity, thus it satisfies the condition

$$\psi^p(x, t) = -U_1^\infty(t)y^\pm(x_1, t) - \int_{+a}^{x_1} \nabla_t y^\pm(x_1', t)\, dx_1'$$

$$|x_1| \leqq a, \qquad x_2 = 0 \tag{9.6}$$

This flow, of course, should not have a jump at the sheet base.

The second contribution $\chi^s(x, t)$ should have the appropriate circulation at the sheet base, thus

$$\hat{\phi}^s(x, t) = -g(x_1 - X_1^\infty(t)) \tag{9.7}$$

while at the profile base

$$\psi^s(x_1, t) = 0 \quad \text{for} \quad |x_1| \leqq a, \qquad x_2 = 0 \tag{9.8}$$

The condition

$$\psi(x, t) = -U_1^\infty(t)y(x, t) - \int_{+a}^{x_1} \nabla_t y(x_1', t)\, dx_1', \qquad x_1 \geqq a, \qquad x_2 = 0 \tag{9.9}$$

on the sheet base, serves on the one hand to insure the continuity of ψ at the sheet base and on the other hand to determine the position $y(x, t)$ of the sheet.

As in chapter 8, cf. (8.17), the Kutta condition will be formulated through the relation

$$\frac{d\chi^p}{d\zeta} + \frac{d\chi^s}{d\zeta} = 0 \qquad \text{at } \zeta = 1 \tag{9.10}$$

with reference to the variable ζ connected with the complex variable

$$z = x_1 + ix_2 \tag{9.11}$$

by

$$z = \frac{a}{2}(\zeta + \zeta^{-1}) \tag{9.12}$$

The function χ^p of z or ζ is determined as in the previous section; it may be represented in the form

$$\chi^p = \sum_{n=0}^{\infty} c_n \zeta^{-n} \qquad (9.13)$$

in which the coefficients c_n can be determined by the Fourier expansion of the profile function $y^{\pm}(a\cos\theta, t)$. Note that this flow should have no circulation. The complex potential of the previous problem was

$$\chi = \frac{i\Gamma^p}{2\pi} \log\zeta + \chi^p \qquad (9.14)$$

where the Γ^p is the counter circulation of the previous problem, cf. (8.13). The counter circulation

$$\cdot\Gamma^p = 2\pi i \frac{d\chi^p}{d\zeta}\bigg|^{\zeta=1} \qquad (9.15)$$

which we shall now call the "effective circulation", was derived from the condition that $d\chi/d\zeta = 0$ at $\zeta = 1$; the effective circulation was given by

$$\Gamma^p = 2\pi \sum_{n=0}^{\infty} nb_n \qquad (9.16)$$

cf. (8.20). Together with $y^{\pm}(x_1, t)$, Γ^p also depends on t.

Having determined this function $\Gamma^p(t)$ we may bring the Kutta condition (9.10) into the form

$$2\pi i \frac{d\chi^s}{d\zeta}\bigg|^{\zeta=1} = -\Gamma^p(t) \qquad (9.17)$$

We proceed to determine the second contribution $\chi^s(z, t)$ to the complex potential function. To this end we map the slit $|x_1| \leq a, x_2 = 0$ onto the unit circle by (9.12) and reflect the unknown vortex distribution about the unit circle by an inversion. The complex potential of the resulting vortex distribution is

$$\chi^s(z, t) = \frac{1}{2\pi i} \int_{x_1'=a}^{x_1'=\infty} \log\frac{\zeta-\xi_1'}{\zeta\xi_1'-1} \, dg(x_1' - X_1^{\infty}(t)) \qquad (9.18)$$

Note that the argument of the logarithm is never negative when $\zeta' = \xi_1' + i\eta_1'$ is outside the unit circle except when ζ is real positive and $\text{Re}(\zeta) < \text{Re}(\zeta')$. If ζ approaches this part of the positive real axis with positive and negative imaginary part the argument of the logarithm approaches the negative real part also with positive and negative imaginary part respectively. Consequently, the jump of the logarithm is $2\pi i$ and hence the jump of $\chi^s(z,t)$ is

$$\hat{\chi}^s(z,t) = \int_{x_1'=x_1}^{\infty} dg(x_1' - X_1^\infty(t)) = -g(x_1 - X_1^\infty(t)) \qquad (9.19)$$

$$\text{(when } x_2 = 0)$$

in agreement with (9.7) and (9.9).

When $|\zeta| = 1$, the argument of the logarithm is in the unit circle hence

$$\text{Im}\,\chi^s(z,t) = 0 \quad \text{for } |x_1| < a, \qquad x_2 = 0 \qquad (9.20)$$

since in (9.18) the logarithm becomes purely imaginary making χ^s real.

As z approaches infinity, finally, $\chi^s(z,t)$ approaches a finite value

$$\lim_{z \to \infty} \chi^s(z,t) = -\frac{1}{2\pi i} \int_{x_1'=a}^{\infty} \log \xi' \, dg(x_1' - X_1^\infty(t)) \qquad (9.21)$$

The quantity $d\chi^p/d\zeta$ which enters the Kutta condition (9.15) can now be calculated from (9.18). We find

$$\frac{d\chi^s(z,t)}{d\zeta} = \frac{1}{2\pi i} \int_{x_1'=a}^{x_1'=\infty} \frac{\xi_1'^2 - 1}{(\zeta\xi_1' - 1)(\zeta - \xi_1')} \, dg(x_1' - X_1^\infty(t)) \qquad (9.22)$$

so that

$$\frac{d\chi^s(z,t)}{d\zeta}\bigg|^{\zeta=1} = -\frac{1}{2\pi i} \int_{x_1'=a}^{x_1'=\infty} \frac{\xi_1' + 1}{\xi_1' - 1} \, dg(x_1' - X_1^\infty(t)) \qquad (9.23)$$

Since the transformation $z = a(\zeta + \zeta^{-1})/2$ implies the relation

$$\frac{\zeta+1}{\zeta-1} = \sqrt{\frac{z+a}{z-a}} \qquad (9.24)$$

we may write condition (9.17) in the form

$$\int_a^\infty \sqrt{\left(\frac{x_1'+a}{x_1'-a}\right)} \, dg(x_1' - X_1^\infty(t)) = \Gamma^p(t) \qquad (9.25)$$

using (9.23).

We assume that the motion starts from rest at the time $t = 0$. The circulation $g(\xi)$ is then zero for $\xi > a$. Consequently, we may substitute

$a + X_1^\infty(t)$ for the upper limit of integration in (9.25) in place of ∞. The resulting relation

$$\int_{x_1=a}^{x_1=a+X_1^\infty(t)} \sqrt{\left(\frac{x_1+a}{x_1-a}\right)} \, dg(x_1 - X_1^\infty(t)) = \Gamma^p(t) \tag{9.26}$$

may be considered as an *integral equation* for the unknown function $g(\xi)$. We recall that the value of $\Gamma^p(t)$ has already been determined.

This integral equation can be solved quite generally by means of the *Laplace transformation*.

Let us first assume that a function $g(\xi)$ is known such that relation (9.26) holds. We then multiply both sides of (9.26) by $\exp\{-\tau X_1^\infty(t)\}$ $dX_1^\infty(t)$ and integrate from the time $t = 0$ when $X_1^\infty(t) = 0$ to the time $t = \infty$ when $X_1^\infty(t)$ becomes infinite. Setting

$$\int_{t=0}^{\infty} \Gamma^p(t) \exp(-\tau X_1^\infty(t)) \, dX_1^\infty(t) = \eta(\tau) \tag{9.27}$$

and $X_1^\infty(t) = X$ on the left member, we obtain the relation

$$\int_0^\infty \left[\int_a^{a+X} \sqrt{\left(\frac{x_1+a}{x_1-a}\right)} \, dg(x_1 - X) \right] e^{-\tau X} dX = \eta(\tau)$$

We now introduce the variable $\xi = x_1 - X$ instead of X and thus bring the left member into the form

$$\int_a^\infty \int_{-\infty}^a \sqrt{\left(\frac{x_1+a}{x_1-a}\right)} e^{\tau(\xi-x_1)} \, dg(\xi) \, dx_1$$

We observe that this expression splits into two factors

$$aH(a\tau)G(\tau) = \eta(\tau) \tag{9.28}$$

with

$$\int_{-\infty}^a e^{\tau\xi} \, dg(\xi) = G(\tau) \tag{9.29}$$

and

$$\int_1^\infty \sqrt{\left(\frac{\alpha+1}{\alpha-1}\right)} e^{-\sigma\alpha} d\alpha = H(\sigma) \tag{9.30}$$

Here we have set $x_1 = a\alpha$, $\sigma = a\tau$.

The function $\eta(\tau)$ is given through (9.27), while $H(\sigma)$ is a universal function which we shall discuss below. The function $G(\tau)$ is related to the function $g(\xi)$ by (9.29).

Suppose now that we define $G(\tau)$ by (9.28) in terms of $\eta(\tau)$ and $H(\sigma)$. Then we maintain that the function

$$g(\xi) = \frac{1}{2\pi i}\int_{Br} G(\tau)\, e^{-\tau\xi}\frac{d\tau}{\tau}$$

or
$$g(\xi) = \frac{1}{2\pi i}\int_{Br}\eta(\tau)\, e^{-\tau\xi}\frac{d\tau}{a\tau H(a\tau)} \tag{9.31}$$

satisfies relation (9.29) provided that the function $\eta(\tau)$ satisfies appropriate conditions. The path "Br", the Bromwich path, may be taken as any straight line, $\mathrm{Re}\tau = \tau_1 > 0$, parallel to the imaginary axis in the right half plane.

We may impose on $\eta(\tau)$ the condition that the function $\tau\eta(\tau)$ be regular in the right half plane and approach a finite constant as τ approaches infinity with $\mathrm{Re}\tau > 0$. As a matter of fact we see from (9.27) after integrating by parts that

$$\tau\eta(\tau) \to \Gamma^p(0) \quad \text{as } \tau \to \infty \tag{9.32}$$

The function $H(\sigma)$ does not vanish for $\mathrm{Re}(\sigma) > 0$ and

$$\sqrt{\left(\frac{\sigma}{2\pi}\right)}e^{\sigma}H(\sigma) \to 1 \quad \text{as } \sigma \to \infty\, \mathrm{Re}\,\sigma > 0 \tag{9.33}$$

as will be shown below. Accordingly the function $\eta(\tau)/H(a\tau)$ is also regular for $\mathrm{Re}\tau > 0$ and $\sqrt{(2\pi)}\sqrt{(a\tau)}\, e^{-a\tau}\eta(\tau)/H(a\tau)$ approaches a finite constant, $a\Gamma^p(0)$, as τ approaches infinity. It then follows from the theory of the Laplace transformation (cf. McLachlan, N. W.: *Modern Operational Calculus*) that the function $g(\xi)$ as given by (9.31) vanishes for $\xi > a$ and further that relation (9.29) holds. It also follows that the integral equation (9.27) is satisfied.

The *universal function* $H(\sigma)$ can be evaluated explicitly. Before giving this explicit evaluation we shall derive the asymptotic behavior of $H(\sigma)$ as $\sigma \to 0$ and as $\sigma \to \infty$ from the representation (9.30).

In order to determine the behavior of $H(\sigma)$ near $\sigma = 0$ we write

$$H(\sigma) = \int_2^{\infty}\sqrt{\left(\frac{\alpha+1}{\alpha-1}\right)}e^{-\sigma\alpha}\, d\alpha + \int_1^2 \sqrt{\left(\frac{\alpha+1}{\alpha-1}\right)}e^{-\sigma\alpha}\, d\alpha$$

or
$$H(\sigma) \cong \int_2^{\infty}\left\{1+\frac{1}{\alpha}\right\}e^{-\sigma\alpha}\, d\alpha + \mathcal{K}(\sigma)$$

We readily verify that the function $\mathscr{K}(\sigma)$ approaches a finite value as $\sigma \to 0$. Evaluating the first integral we find the formula

$$H(\sigma) \cong \sigma^{-1} e^{-2\sigma} - e^{-2\sigma} \log 2 + \sigma \int_2^\infty \log \alpha\, e^{-\sigma\alpha}\, d\alpha + \mathscr{K}(\sigma)$$

$$\cong \sigma^{-1} e^{-2\sigma} - e^{-2\sigma} \log 2 + \int_{2\sigma}^\infty \log \frac{\tau}{\sigma} e^{-\tau}\, d\tau + \mathscr{K}(\sigma)$$

$$\cong \sigma^{-1} e^{-2\sigma} - e^{-2\sigma} \log 2\sigma + \int_{2\sigma}^\infty \log \tau\, e^{-\tau}\, d\tau + \mathscr{K}(\sigma)$$

or
$$H(\sigma) \cong \frac{1}{\sigma} - \log \sigma + \mathscr{K}_1(\sigma) \tag{9.34}$$

where again the function $\mathscr{K}_1(\sigma)$ approaches a finite value as $\sigma \to 0$. As a matter of fact

$$\mathscr{K}_1(\sigma) = \int_{2\sigma}^\infty \log \tau\, e^{-\tau}\, d\tau + \int_1^2 \sqrt{\left(\frac{\alpha+1}{\alpha-1}\right)} e^{-\sigma\alpha}\, d\alpha - e^{-2\sigma} \log 2$$

For large values of σ we set $\alpha = 1 + \beta^2$ and obtain

$$e^\sigma H(\sigma) = 2 \int_0^\infty \sqrt{(2+\beta^2)}\, e^{-\sigma\beta^2}\, d\beta$$

$$= 2\sqrt{2} \int_0^\infty e^{-\sigma\beta^2}\, d\beta + \sigma^{-\frac{3}{2}} \mathscr{J}(\sigma)$$

One readily verifies that the function

$$\mathscr{J}(\sigma) = 2 \int_0^\infty \frac{\beta_1^2}{\sqrt{(2+\sigma^{-1}\beta_1^2)}+\sqrt{2}} e^{-\beta_1^2}\, d\beta_1$$

approaches a finite value as $\sigma \to \infty$. Consequently, we have

$$H(\sigma) = e^{-\sigma} \left[\sqrt{\left(\frac{2\pi}{\sigma}\right)} + \sigma^{-\frac{3}{2}} \mathscr{J}(\sigma) \right] \tag{9.35}$$

whence, in particular,

$$\sqrt{\left(\frac{\sigma}{2\pi}\right)} e^\sigma H(\sigma) \to 1 \quad \text{as } \sigma \to \infty, \qquad \text{Re}\, \sigma > 0 \tag{9.36}$$

We have thus shown relation (9.33) to hold.

More delicate considerations would be needed in order to prove that the function $H(\tau)$ does not vanish in the right half plane, nor on the imaginary axis. Assuming that this is so we may conclude that the function $g(\xi)$ is defined by (9.31).

As remarked previously the function $H(\tau)$ can be given explicitly, namely, as

$$H(\sigma) = \frac{\pi}{2}\left[iH_0^{(1)}(i\sigma) - H_1^{(2)}(-i\sigma)\right]$$

where $H_0^{(1)}$ and $H_1^{(2)}$ are the first and second Hankel functions of order zero and one; cf. Watson: *Bessel functions*.[1] The known behavior of these functions for $\tau \sim \infty$ and $\tau \sim 0$ agrees with formulae (9.34) and (9.35).

From relation (9.36) we can derive the behavior of the function $g(\xi)$ near $\xi = a$. We deform the path of integration in (9.31) parallel to itself letting $\mathrm{Re}\,\tau$ approach infinity. From (9.32) and (9.36) we conclude that the function $\eta(\tau)/a\tau H(a\tau)$ behaves like $\Gamma^p(0)\,e^{a\tau}/\sqrt{(2\pi a\tau^3)}$ as $\tau \to \infty$. Hence $g(\xi)$ behaves like

$$\frac{\Gamma^p(0)}{2\pi i}\int_{\mathrm{Br}} e^{(a-\xi)\sigma}\frac{d\sigma}{a\sqrt{(2\pi a\sigma)}}$$

i.e.
$$g(\xi) \sim \frac{2}{\pi}\sqrt{\left(\frac{a-\xi}{2a}\right)}\Gamma^p(0) \quad \text{for } \xi \sim a, \qquad \xi \leqq a \qquad (9.37)$$

Thus we see that the circulation starts to grow like

$$\sqrt{(a-\xi)} = \sqrt{(a-x_1 + X_1^\infty(t))} \text{ unless } \Gamma^p(0) = 0$$

The behavior of $g(\xi)$ for large values of ξ and t will be discussed in connection with the special problems treated in the following chapters.

[1] Substitute in 6.22 formulae (10) and (11), p. 180 of Watson.

CHAPTER 10

Accelerating Wing—First Order Theory

We first consider the special case in which the airfoil is at rest up to the time $t = 0$ and is then accelerated instantaneously to a velocity which remains constant from then on. In this very special case we shall be able to solve the integral equation (9.25).

The constant velocity of the airfoil after the time $t = 0$ will be denoted by

$$-U^\infty = \{-U_1^\infty, 0, 0\} \tag{10.1}$$

At the time $t = 0$ the base of the airfoil is assumed to cover the segment $|x_1| \leq a, x_2 = 0$. The main motion $X^a(t) = -X^\infty(t)$ is assumed to be the motion of the midpoint $x = 0$ and hence it will be given by

$$X_1^\infty(t) = U_1^\infty t, \qquad X_2^\infty(t) = 0, \qquad t > 0 \tag{10.2}$$

supposing, of course, that the center of the airfoil is at the origin at the beginning of the motion.

The circulation Γ^p is a constant from $t = 0$ on and hence the function $\eta(\sigma)$ defined by (9.27) becomes

$$\eta(\sigma) = \Gamma^p \int_0^\infty e^{-\sigma x}\, dx$$

or
$$\eta(\sigma) = \sigma^{-1} \Gamma^p \tag{10.3}$$

The function $g(\xi)$, given by (9.31), becomes

$$g(\xi) = \frac{\Gamma^p}{2\pi i a} \int_{Br} e^{-\sigma\xi} \frac{d\sigma}{\sigma^2 H(a\sigma)} \tag{10.4}$$

The behavior of this function for large values of ξ can be derived from the behavior of $H(\tau)$ at $\tau = 0$, given by (9.34). We deform the path of integration in (10.4) into the origin leaving out the origin by letting the path run over a little arc $\mathscr{A}$: $\sigma = \varepsilon e^{i\theta}, -\pi/2 \leq \theta \leq \pi/2$ around the

65

origin in the right half plane. Asymptotically, only the integral over this arc contributes; i.e. asymptotically

$$g(\xi) \sim \frac{\Gamma^p}{2\pi i} \int_{\mathscr{A}} e^{-\sigma\xi}[1 + a\sigma \log a\sigma]\sigma^{-1} d\sigma \qquad (10.5)$$

since, according to (9.34),

$$[H(\tau)]^{-1} \sim \tau[1 + \tau \log \tau]$$

Without changing the asymptotic behavior of the right member of (10.5) to the path $\mathscr{A}$ can be augmented by letting it come from $-\infty$ below the negative real axis, skirt the origin along $\mathscr{A}$, and return to $-\infty$ above the negative real axis. The resulting integral can then be evaluated. Thus we find

$$g(\xi) \sim \Gamma^p \left[\frac{1}{2\pi i} \oint e^{-\sigma\xi} \sigma^{-1} d\sigma + a \int_0^{-\infty} e^{-\sigma\xi} d\sigma \right] = \Gamma^p \left[1 + \frac{a}{\xi} \right]$$

or, what is equivalent,

$$g(\xi) \sim \Gamma^p \left[1 - \frac{a}{a-\xi} \right] \text{ as } a - \xi \sim \infty \qquad (10.6)$$

Thus it is, in particular, seen that *eventually the counter circulation $g(x_1 - U_1^\infty t)$ approaches the value Γ^p which the flow acquires according to the Kutta-Jukowski theory.*

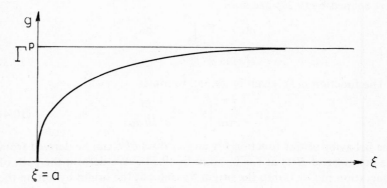

Fig. 10.1.

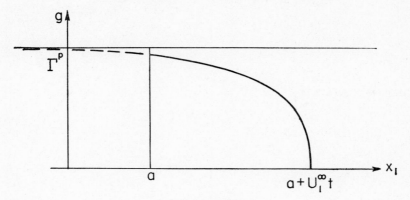

Fig. 10.2.

CHAPTER 11

Oscillatory Wing—Flutter

Next we consider a more general type of motion, in particular oscillatory motion, of the airfoil. For simplicity we assume that the trailing edge keeps its relative position. Denoting the angle of attack by $\alpha = \alpha(t)$ we describe the position of the airfoil by

$$y^{\pm}(x,t) = y_0^{\pm}(x_1) + \alpha(t)(a-x_1) \tag{11.1}$$

which $y_0^{\pm}(x_1)$ describes the "zero position" of the airfoil. As before we assume that the main motion starts instantaneously at the time $t = 0$ and then has a constant velocity $U^a = -U^{\infty} = -\{U_1^{\infty}, 0, 0\}$.

The condition of sliding takes the form

$$U_2^{\pm}(x_1,t) = U_1^{\infty}\nabla_1 y_0^{\pm}(x_1) - U_1^{\infty}\alpha(t) + \nabla_t \alpha(t)(a-x_1) \tag{11.2}$$

see (I°, p. 49), or, by (9.1),

$$\psi^{\pm}(x_1,t) = -U_1^{\infty} y_0^{\pm}(x_1) - U_1^{\infty}\alpha(t)(a-x_1) + \tfrac{1}{2}\nabla_t \alpha(t)\{(a-x_1)^2\} \tag{11.3}$$

except for an irrelevant additional constant.

The complex potential $\chi(z,t)$ may be obtained as the sum

$$\chi = \chi_0 + \chi_1 + \chi_2 \tag{11.4}$$

of three contributions corresponding to the right members of (11.3). As before each of these three functions χ will be obtained as the sum $\chi = \chi^p + \chi^s$ of contributions due to the profile and due to the sheet. The values $\Gamma^p(t)$ of the circulation, given by (9.15) will be obtained as

$$\Gamma^p(t) = \Gamma_0^p + \Gamma_1^p(t) + \Gamma_2^p(t) \tag{11.5}$$

The contribution χ_0 is identical with the one considered in chapter 10; its effect is the build-up of the final circulation which the airfoil would

69

attain if it did not oscillate. In the following we shall disregard this contribution.

The complex potentials χ_1^p and χ_2^p can be given explicitly in terms of the variable ζ connected with $z = x_1 + ix_2$ by

$$z = \frac{a}{2}(\zeta + \zeta^{-1})$$

We have

$$\chi_1^p = -iU_1^\infty \alpha(t)a[1 - \zeta^{-1}] \tag{11.6}_1$$

and

$$\chi_2^p = +\frac{i}{2}\nabla_t \alpha a^2[\tfrac{3}{2} - 2\zeta^{-1} + \tfrac{1}{2}\zeta^{-2}] \tag{11.6}_2$$

for, on $\zeta = e^{i\theta}$, the imaginary part of these functions becomes

$$\psi_1^p = -U_1^\infty \alpha(t)a[1 - \cos\theta] = -U_1^\infty \alpha(t)[a - x_1]$$

and

$$\psi_2^p = +\tfrac{1}{2}\nabla_t \alpha a^2[\tfrac{3}{2} - 2\cos\theta + \tfrac{1}{2}\cos 2\theta]$$

$$= +\tfrac{1}{2}\nabla_t \alpha a^2[1 - 2\cos\theta + \cos^2\theta]$$

$$= +\tfrac{1}{2}\nabla_t \alpha(t)\{[a - x_1]^2\}$$

in agreement with (11.3).

The effective circulations $\Gamma_{1,2}^p$, given by (9.15), are then found to be

$$\Gamma_1^p = +2\pi U_1^\infty a\alpha(t) \tag{11.7}_1$$

$$\Gamma_2^p = -\pi a^2 \nabla_t \alpha(t) \tag{11.7}_2$$

Next we determine the transforms $\eta_1(\sigma), \eta_2(\sigma)$ according to (9.27)

$$\eta_1(\sigma) = 2\pi(U_1^\infty)^2 a \int_0^\infty \alpha(t)\exp(-\sigma U_1^\infty t)\,dt \tag{11.8}_1$$

$$\eta_2(\sigma) = -\pi U_1^\infty a^2 \int_0^\infty \nabla_t \alpha(t)\exp(-\sigma U_1^\infty t)\,dt \tag{11.8}_2$$

$$= -\tfrac{1}{2}a\sigma\eta_1(\sigma)$$

assuming $\alpha(0) = 0$ and recalling that $x_1 = U_1^\infty t$.

We shall now make the special assumption that the motion of the airplane is oscillatory in such a way that

$$\alpha(t) = \alpha_0 \sin\beta t \tag{11.9}$$

Then we obtain

$$\eta_1(\sigma) = +2\pi(U_1^\infty)^2 \, a\alpha_0 \frac{\beta}{\beta^2 + (U_1^\infty)^2 \sigma^2} \qquad (11.10)_1$$

$$\eta_2(\sigma) = -\pi(U_1^\infty)^2 \, a^2 \alpha_0 \frac{\beta\sigma}{\beta^2 + (U_1^\infty)^2 \sigma^2} \qquad (11.10)_2$$

We are particularly interested in the asymptotic behavior of the functions $g_1(\xi)$ and $g_2(\xi)$ given by

$$g(\xi) = \frac{1}{2\pi i} \int_{\text{Br}} \eta(\tau) e^{-\tau\xi} \frac{d\tau}{a\tau H(a\tau)} \qquad (9.31)$$

To this end we try to deform the path of integration Br into the left half plane. This is prevented by the poles which the functions $\eta_1(\sigma)$ and $\eta_2(\sigma)$ have at the points $\sigma = \pm i(U_1^\infty)^{-1}\beta$ in addition to the singularity at $\sigma = 0$ of the integrand. Since these functions remain finite at $\sigma = 0$ no contribution results from this point. The contributions from the poles then lead to the asymptotic formulae

$$g_1(\xi) = -\text{Re}\{2\pi U_1^\infty \, a\alpha_0 \, e^{i\kappa\xi/a}[\kappa H(-i\kappa)]^{-1}\} \qquad (11.11)_1$$

$$g_2(\xi) = +\text{Re}\{i\pi a^2 \, \beta\alpha_0 \, [\kappa H(-i\kappa)]^{-1} e^{i\kappa\xi/a}\} \qquad (11.11)_2$$

with
$$\kappa = a\beta(U_1^\infty)^{-1} \qquad (11.12)$$

Thus it is seen that the sheet circulation is oscillatory with the wave length $2\pi a/\kappa = 2\pi U_1^\infty/\beta$.

The asymptotic behavior of the flow can then be determined from formula (9.18) by using the expressions (11.11) for the circulation functions $g_i(\xi)$.

After having determined the flow past an airfoil one can calculate the forces exerted by the fluid on it. For an airfoil of a given shape these forces depend on the position and the velocity of the airfoil. In addition to these aerodynamic forces elastic forces act on the airfoil depending on the structure of the wing and the way in which it is built into the fuselage.

Assuming that these forces are also known in their dependence on position and velocity of the airfoil one may formulate the problem of determining the motion of the wing under the influence of the forces acting on it. Since the aerodynamic forces are not conservative it may happen that the motion of the wing is unstable; (actually this will happen only if the wing consists of several parts, such as a main wing and an aileron). The motion is called stable if all movements are oscillatory or damped; it is called unstable if a movement with unbounded amplitude exists. The motion of a wing of the latter type is called "flutter". The investigation of the circumstances under which flutter may occur is based on the approximation of the flow resulting from oscillatory motion of the wing given in this chapter. Cf. Theodorsen Th.: "General Theory of Aerodynamic Instability and the Mechanism of Flutter", NACA Report 496, 1935.

CHAPTER 12

The Force Exerted by the Fluid on an Airfoil with a Trailing Vortex Sheet

As is usually done in Fluid Dynamics we shall determine the forces exerted by a fluid on an airfoil, by calculating the integral of the pressure acting against the airfoil over its upper and lower surfaces. Since in the approximation considered the airfoil reduces to a surface in the plane $x_2 = 0$ the resultant force would seem to be directed perpendicular to this plane. It is not *a priori* obvious, though, that no horizontal component results from the pressure acting on the leading edge; for if one lets the thickness of the airfoil shrink to zero the pressure at the leading edge becomes infinite and the horizontal component of the resultant force might be different from zero in the limit. A closer examination would show, however, that this is not the case in the present problem.

In the approximation considered the pressure is given by Bernoulli's law [cf. (2.7)] as

$$p = -\rho[\nabla_t \phi + U_1^\infty \nabla_1 \phi] + \text{const.}$$

and hence the pressure difference at the base of the profile is given by

$$\hat{p} = -\rho[\nabla_t \hat{\phi} + U_1^\infty \nabla_1 \hat{\phi}] \tag{12.1}$$

We confine ourselves to the task of determining the contribution $\hat{p}^s$ to this pressure difference which results from the shed vorticity,

$$\hat{p}^s = -\rho[\nabla_t \hat{\phi}^s + U_1^\infty \nabla_1 \hat{\phi}^s] \tag{12.2}$$

for, this contribution seems to dominate the contribution resulting from the flow χ^p.

From the formula (9.18) with $X_1^\infty(t) = U_1^\infty t$ we have

$$\phi^s(z,t) = \operatorname{Re} \frac{1}{2\pi i} \int_{z'=a}^\infty \log \frac{\zeta-\zeta'}{\zeta\zeta'-1} \, dg(x_1' - U_1^\infty t)$$

where

$$z = \frac{a}{2}\left(\zeta + \frac{1}{\zeta}\right), \qquad \zeta = e^{i\theta}$$

$$z' = \frac{a}{2}\left(\zeta' + \frac{1}{\zeta'}\right), \qquad \zeta' = \zeta_1'$$

In calculating $\nabla_t \phi^s$ we use the relation

$$\nabla_t g(x_1' - U_1^\infty t) = -U_1^\infty \nabla_{x_1'} g(x_1' - U_1^\infty t)$$

Upon integration by parts we find

$$\nabla_t \phi^s + U_1^\infty \nabla_{x_1} \phi^s$$

$$= U_1^\infty \operatorname{Re} \frac{1}{2\pi i} \int_{z'=a}^\infty (\nabla_{x_1'} + \nabla_{x_1}) \log \frac{\zeta-\zeta'}{\zeta\zeta'-1} dg(x_1' - U_1^\infty t)$$

A simple calculation shows that

$$(\nabla_{x_1'} + \nabla_{x_1}) \log \frac{\zeta-\zeta'}{\zeta\zeta'-1} = \pm i \frac{z+z'}{\sqrt{(a^2-z^2)}\sqrt{(z'^2-a^2)}}$$

$$= \pm i \frac{x_1 + x_1'}{\sqrt{(a^2-x_1^2)}\sqrt{((x_1')^2-a^2)}} \qquad \theta \gtrless 0$$

Thus, indicating the jump by [ ], we see that

$$\left[(\nabla_{x_1'} + \nabla_{x_1}) \log \frac{\zeta-\zeta'}{\zeta\zeta'-1}\right] = 2i \frac{x_1 - x_1'}{\sqrt{(a^2-x_1^2)}\sqrt{((x_1')^2-a^2)}}$$

so that

$$\hat{p}^s = -\rho U_1^\infty \frac{1}{\pi} \int_{x_1'=a}^\infty \frac{x_1 - x_1'}{\sqrt{(a^2-x_1^2)}\sqrt{((x_1')^2-a)}} \, dg(x_1' - U_1^\infty t) \quad (12.3)$$

The resultant force $F(t) = \{0, F_2(t)\}$ is calculated by integration with respect to x_1 from $-a$ to a; we thus get

$$F_2(t) = -\rho U_1^\infty \int_{x_1'=a}^\infty \frac{x_1'}{\sqrt{((x_1')^2-a)}} \, dg(x_1' - U_1^\infty t) \qquad (12.4)$$

In a similar way one could derive from (12.3) the moment of the forces exerted by the fluid on the airfoil.

In the special problem of the *instantaneously accelerated airfoil* the behavior of the *lift* $F_2(t)$ after a long time can easily be calculated. It was found at the end of chapter 11 that the bulk of the shed vorticity is concentrated at the tip of the vortex sheet and that $dg(x_1 - U_1^\infty t)$ approaches zero at each fixed point x_1 as $t \to \infty$. Since for large values of x_1 the ratio $x_1'/\sqrt{((x_1')^2 - a^2)}$ approaches the value one, the asymptotic behavior of $F_2(t)$ is given by

$$F_2(t) = -\rho U_1^\infty \int_{-\infty}^{+a+U_1^\infty t} dg(x_1' - U_1^\infty t)$$

or $\qquad F_2(t) = -\rho U_1^\infty \Gamma^p \qquad \text{as } t \to \infty$

in agreement with the Kutta-Joukowski theory (cf. Durand, *Aerodynamic Theory*, vol. 1, p. 171).

In the case of the oscillatory airfoil one obtains oscillatory forces asymptotically when one uses the asymptotic expression for $g(\xi)$ derived at the end of chapter 11.

In calculating the total force exerted on the airfoil it is possible to avoid the calculation of the pressures acting on the airfoil. This is done by expressing the force in a simple manner *in terms of the behavior of the complex velocity potential χ at infinity.* As a matter of fact this can be carried out *even without making the approximation based on the flatness assumption.*

This possibility enables us to avoid the necessity of investigating the force in the direction of the sheet which may arise from the pressure at the leading edge of the airfoil.

We shall confine ourselves to the case of two-dimensional flow in this consideration.

It is convenient to let $X^a = X^a(t)$ be the position of the centroid of the airfoil, so that $x = X - X^a(t)$ is the position of a point relative to the centroid. The velocity of the centroid is

$$U^a(t) = -U_1^\infty(t) = \nabla_t X^a(t)$$

The velocity of the rotational motion of the airfoil is

$$[x, \omega(t)]$$

where $\qquad \omega(t) = \{0, 0, \omega_3(t)\}$

is the vector of angular velocity in negative θ direction of this rotation. The velocity of the point x of the airfoil is therefore

$$U^a(t) + [x, \omega(t)] \tag{12.5}$$

The boundary condition that the fluid slides along the profile is expressed by the condition that the difference of the flow velocity u and the velocity of the profile be tangential to the profile, i.e. by

$$[u, dx] = [U^a(t), dx] + \omega(t)(x\,dx) \tag{12.6}$$

Note that $(\omega(t)\,dx) = 0$, since $\omega_1 = \omega_2 = 0$ and $dx_3 = 0$.

We may describe the flow by a potential function $\phi(x, t)$ or by a stream function $\psi(x, t)$. The velocity u is then given by

$$u = \nabla\phi \quad \text{or } u = \{\nabla_2\psi, -\nabla_1\psi\} \tag{12.7}$$

The boundary condition (12.6) may be conveniently expressed in terms of the function ψ as

$$\psi = [U^a(t), x] + \tfrac{1}{2}\omega(t)|x|^2 + c(t); \tag{12.8}$$

for, the tangential differential of both sides of (12.8) are exactly both sides of relation (12.6).

Next we introduce the complex variable $z = x_1 + ix_2$, the complex potential $\chi = \phi + i\psi$ and the complex velocity $w = u + iv$ with $\bar{w} = \partial\chi/dz$. According to our assumptions about the flow, w vanishes at infinity and hence $\bar{w}$ is regular there. Since the total circulation is zero, $\bar{w}$ vanishes like z^{-2} and hence χ vanishes like z^{-1} at infinity.

We denote by $\mathcal{B}$ the boundary of the profile $\mathcal{A}$ and by $\mathcal{S}$ the vortex sheet. Instead of the force $F = \{F_1, F_2\}$ exerted by the fluid on the airfoil, we calculate the complex force $H = F_1 + iF_2$ and obtain

$$H = -\oint_{\mathcal{B}} p(n_1 + in_2)\,ds \tag{12.9}$$

$$= -\oint_{\mathcal{B}+\mathcal{S}} p(n_1 + in_2)\,ds$$

From the law of conservation of momentum (1.20) we find that

$$\oint_{\mathcal{B}+\mathcal{S}} p(n_1 - in_2)\,ds - \oint_{\infty} p(n_1 + in_2)\,ds$$

$$= \rho\iint \nabla_t w\,dx_1\,dx_2 - \oint_{\mathcal{B}+\mathcal{S}} \rho w(un)\,ds + \oint_{\infty} \rho w(un)\,ds$$

Here the double integral is to be extended over the exterior of $\mathscr{B}+\mathscr{S}$; by $\oint_{\infty} \ldots ds$ we mean the limit which the integral over a large circle approaches when its radius increases indefinitely. From the behavior of w at ∞ it follows that $\oint_{\infty} \rho w(un)\, ds$ is zero. It could also be shown that $-\int_{\mathscr{B}+\mathscr{S}} \rho w(un)\, ds$ could be combined with the double integral so as to give

$$\rho \nabla_t \iint w\, dx_1\, dx_2$$

Note that the contours $\mathscr{B}$ and $\mathscr{S}$ depend on the time! We thus obtain the relation

$$H = -\rho \nabla_t \iint w\, dx_1\, dx_2 - \oint_{\infty} p(n_1 + in_2)\, ds$$

Next we make use of Bernoulli's law

$$p = -\rho(\nabla_t \phi + \tfrac{1}{2}|w|^2) + p_0(t)$$

and express the velocity (cf. (12.7))

$$w = -i(\nabla_1 + i\nabla_2)\psi$$

in terms of the stream function ψ.

After using Gauss' theorem we obtain

$$H = \rho \nabla_t \left\{ -i \oint_{\mathscr{B}+\mathscr{S}} \psi(n_1 + in_2)\, ds + \oint_{\infty} \chi(n_1 + in_2)\, ds \right\} \quad (12.10)$$

again making use of the behavior of w at infinity. Also we have set

$$\oint_{\infty} \nabla_t \phi(n_1 + in_2)\, ds = \nabla_t \oint_{\infty} \phi(n_1 - in_2)\, ds$$

which was permitted since the contour at infinity can be chosen to be independent of the time.

The integral at infinity occurring in (12.10) can be written as a complex integral

$$\oint_{\infty} \chi(n_1 + in_2)\, ds = -i \oint_{\infty} \chi\, dz \quad (12.11)$$

It is thus given by the first term of the expansion of χ with respect to powers of z^{-1}.

In order to evaluate the first integral in (12.10) we make use of the fact that the function ψ is continuous on the sheet $\mathscr{S}$ and is given on the profile $\mathscr{P}$ by (12.8). We readily verify the relations

$$\int_{\mathscr{B}} [U^a, x](n_1 + in_2)\, ds = iW^a A$$

where A is the area of the airfoil and

$$W^a = U_1^a + iU_2^a$$

further,

$$\frac{1}{2}\int_{\mathscr{B}} |x|^2 (n_1 + in_2)\, ds = \int_{\mathscr{A}} \int z\, dx_1\, dx_2$$

The latter term vanishes since the origin was chosen to be the center of mass. Consequently, we obtain from (12.11) the relation

$$-i\oint_{\mathscr{B}} \psi(n_1 + in_2)\, ds = AW^a$$

Insertion into (12.10) yields the final expression

$$H = \rho \nabla_t \left\{ AW^a - i\oint_\infty \chi\, dz \right\} \tag{12.12}$$

If the last term here were absent we could write the equation of motion of the airfoil as

$$(M_0 + \rho A)\nabla_t W^a = H_1$$

where M_0 is its mass and H_1 are other than aerodynamic forces. In that case $M_0 + \rho A$ could be called the apparent mass of the airfoil. Actually however, this last term in (12.12) does not vanish, in fact M_0 partly cancels with the term AW^a.

In applying this formula we shall employ the approximation procedure for flat airfoils and set $\chi = \chi^p + \chi^s$. We also take again the midpoint and not the centroid as the origin.

We shall first calculate the contribution

$$H^{(s)} = -i\rho \nabla_t \oint_\infty \chi^{(s)}\, dz$$

due to the shed vortices. From formula (9.18) we derive the expression

$$\chi^{(s)} = \frac{1}{2\pi i} \int_{x_1'=a}^{\infty} \left\{ -\log \xi_1' + \frac{1}{\zeta}\left(\frac{1}{\xi_1'} - \xi_1'\right) \right\} dg(x_1' - U_1^\infty t)$$

for the behavior of $\chi^{(s)}$ for large values of ζ or $z = \frac{a}{2}(\zeta + \zeta^{-1})$. Since

$$\frac{1}{2\pi i} \oint_\infty \zeta^{-1} dz = \frac{a}{2} \qquad (12.13)$$

we obtain

$$\oint_\infty \chi^{(s)} dz = \frac{a}{2} \int_{x_1'=a}^{\infty} \left(\frac{1}{\xi_1'} - \xi_1'\right) dg(x_1' - U_1^\infty t)$$

or, since

$$\xi_1' - \frac{1}{\xi_1'} = \frac{2}{a}\sqrt{((x_1')^2 - a^2)}$$

$$\oint_\infty \chi^{(s)} dz = -\int_{x_1'=a}^{\infty} \sqrt{((x_1')^2 - a^2)}) \, dg(x_1' - U_1^\infty t) \qquad (12.14)$$

and

$$H^{(s)} = i\rho \nabla_t \int_{x_1'=a}^{\infty} \sqrt{((x_1')^2 - a^2)} \, dg(x_1' - U_1^\infty t) \qquad (12.15)$$

Observing the relation $(\nabla_t + U_1^\infty \nabla_{x_1'}) g(x_1' - U_1^\infty t) = 0$ and using integration by parts

$$H^{(s)} = i\rho U_1^\infty \int_{x_1'=a}^{\infty} \frac{x_1'}{\sqrt{((x_1')^2 - a^2)}} \, dg(x_1' - U_1^\infty t) \qquad (12.16)$$

in agreement with formula (12.4).

Next we shall calculate the contribution

$$H^{(p)} = \rho \nabla_t \left[-i \oint_\infty \chi^p \, dz + A U_1^a \right] \qquad (12.17)$$

which depends on the nature of the profile.

We assume that the potential χ^p is expanded in the form

$$\chi^p = c_1 \zeta^{-1} + \dots$$

Then, because of (12.13)

$$-i \oint_\infty \chi^p \, dz = \pi a c_1$$

In order to determine the coefficient c_1 we note that on the circle $\zeta = e^{i\theta}$, the image of the base of the profile,

$$\psi = \operatorname{Im} \chi = \operatorname{Im} c_1 e^{-i\theta} + \ldots = \frac{1}{2i} c_1 e^{-i\theta} - \frac{1}{2i} \bar{c}_1 e^{i\theta} + \ldots$$

Hence c_1 is the coefficient of $e^{-i\theta}$ in the Fourier expansion of the function $2i\psi$. From the condition of sliding (9.6) we have

$$\psi = -U_1^\infty y^\pm (a \cos \theta)$$

hence

$$c_1 = -\frac{i}{\pi} U_1^\infty \left\{ \int_0^{+\pi} e^{i\theta} y^+ (a \cos \theta)\, d\theta + \int_{-\pi}^0 e^{i\theta} y^- (a \cos \theta)\, d\theta \right\}$$

$$= \frac{1}{\pi a} U_1^\infty \left[A - i \int_{-a}^{+a} 2\tilde{y}(x_1) \frac{x_1\, dx_1}{\sqrt{(a^2 - x_1^2)}} \right]$$

where

$$A = \int_{-a}^{+a} \hat{y}(x_1)\, dx_1 \tag{12.18}$$

is the area of the profile.

Consequently

$$-i \oint_\infty \chi^p\, dz = U_1^\infty \left[A - i \int_{-a}^{+a} 2\tilde{y}(x_1) \frac{x_1\, dx_1}{\sqrt{(a^2 - x_1^2)}} \right]$$

In view of the relation

$$U_1^a = -U_1^\infty$$

we see that the term U_1^a occurring in (12.17) cancels with the real part of $-i \oint_\infty \chi^p\, dz$. Hence we finally obtain the expression

$$H^{(p)} = -i\rho \nabla_t \int_{-a}^{+a} 2\tilde{y}(x_1) \frac{x_1\, dx_1}{\sqrt{(a^2 - x_1^2)}} U_1^\infty(t) \tag{12.19}$$

for the contribution of the nature of the profile to the force. The force is then either a positive or negative lift, and we easily see, it is absent if the profile is symmetric or unaccelerated.

CHAPTER 13

Extended Theory of Thin Airfoils[1]

In this section we shall continue the study begun in chapter 8 of flat airfoils of infinite span in two-dimensional potential flow moving with constant velocity U^a in the negative x_1-direction. As in chapter 8, in terms of the new variables $x_1 = X_1 - U^a t$ our problem becomes that of a stationary airfoil in a flow with velocity $(-U^a, 0) = (U_1^\infty, 0)$ at infinity. We shall first suppose that the airfoil is at zero incidence and symmetric about the x_1-axis, see Fig. 13.1, described by the profile functions

$$y^\pm = \pm \varepsilon F(x_1) = \pm \varepsilon x_1^{\frac{1}{2}}(F_0 + F_1 x_1 + \ldots) \quad 0 \leqq x_1 \leqq 1 \quad (13.1)$$

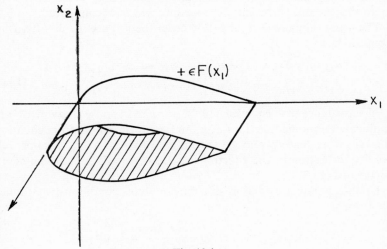

Fig. 13.1.

[1] This section was presented by G. B. Whitham. It is based on the work by M. J. Lighthill: A new approach to Airfoil Theory—*The Aeronautical Quarterly*, Vol. III, Nov. 1951.

We treat incompressible irrotational flow so that the equations of motion are

$$\nabla_1 u_1 + \nabla_2 u_2 = 0$$
$$\nabla_2 u_1 - \nabla_1 u_2 = 0 \tag{13.2}$$

The problem is to find a solution of these equations which satisfies the boundary condition of zero normal velocity on the airfoil surface, i.e.

$$u_2/u_1 = \pm \varepsilon F'(x_1) \quad \text{on } x_2 = \pm \varepsilon F(x_1), \qquad 0 \leq x_1 \leq 1 \tag{13.3}$$

and such that

$$u_1 \to U_1^\infty, \qquad u_2 \to 0 \text{ at infinity} \tag{13.3a}$$

The usual theory of thin airfoils assumes that $u_1 - U_1^\infty$ and u_2 are small, and approximate (13.3) by

$$u_2 = \pm U_1^\infty \varepsilon F'(x_1) \quad \text{on } x_2 = \pm 0, \qquad 0 \leq x_1 \leq 1 \tag{13.3'}$$

then, the solution is easily found. However, it is clear from (13.3') and (13.1) that u_2 is singular like $x_1^{-\frac{1}{2}}$ at the leading edge, $x_1 = 0$; in fact, there should be a stagnation point there with $u_1 = u_2 = 0$. It will now be shown how this failing of the thin airfoil theory may be remedied, and to do this the full perturbation procedure will be reconsidered.

The usual thin airfoil results (first order theory) are the first terms in expansions

$$u_1(x_1, x_2) = U_1^\infty(1 + \varepsilon u_1^{(1)}(x_1, x_2) + \varepsilon^2 u_1^{(2)}(x_1, x_2) + ...)$$
$$u_2(x_1, x_2) = U_1^\infty(\varepsilon u_2^{(1)}(x_1, x_2) + \varepsilon^2 u_2^{(2)}(x_1, x_2) + ...) \tag{13.4}$$

In accordance with equation (13.2), we shall suppose that $u_1^{(i)}$, $u_2^{(i)}$ are conjugate harmonic functions of x_1 and x_2; furthermore from equation (13.3a) we see that $u_1^{(i)}$ and $u_2^{(i)}$ should tend to zero as x_1, x_2 approach infinity, in addition, the functions in (13.4) should satisfy boundary conditions (13.3).

Upon expanding u_2 and u_1 in a Taylor series condition (13.3) takes the form

$$u_2(x_1, 0) \pm \varepsilon F(x_1) u_{2x_2}(x_1, 0) + \frac{\varepsilon^2 F^2(x_1)}{2} u_{2x_2x_2}(x_1, 0) \pm ...$$

$$= \pm(u_1(x_1, 0) \pm \varepsilon F(x_1) u_{1x_2}(x_1, 0) + ...)\varepsilon F'(x_1) \tag{13.5}$$

where x_1 runs along the base of the airfoil, i.e. $0 \leq x_1 \leq 1$. Inserting expansion (13.4) in (13.5) and collecting terms of the same order in ε we see (upon taking the terms of the first, second and third orders, respectively) that on $x_2 = \pm 0, 0 \leq x_1 \leq 1$, the functions $u_1^{(i)}(x_1, x_2)$, $u_2^{(i)}(x, x_2)$ satisfy,

(First order terms)

$$u_2^{(1)} = \pm F'(x_1) \tag{13.6}$$

(Second order terms)

$$u_2^{(2)} \pm F(x_1)u_{2x_2}^{(1)} = \pm F'(x_1)u_1^{(1)} \tag{13.7}$$

(Third order terms)

$$u_2^{(3)} \pm F(x_1)u_{2x_2}^{(2)} + \frac{F^2(x_1)}{2}u_{2x_2x_2}^{(1)} = \pm F'(x_1)u_1^{(2)} + FF'(x_1)u_{1x_2}^{(1)} \tag{13.8}$$

Making use of (13.2) we get,

$$u_2^{(1)}(x_1, \pm 0) = \pm F'(x_1) \tag{13.6}'$$

$$u_2^{(2)}(x_1, \pm 0) = \pm G'(x_1) \tag{13.7}'$$

$$u_2^{(3)}(x_1, \pm 0) = \pm H'(x_1) \tag{13.8}'$$

where $\qquad G(x_1) = F(x_1)u_1^{(1)}(x_1, 0) \tag{13.9}$

and $\qquad H(x_1) = \tfrac{1}{2}F^2(x_1)F''(x_1) + F(x_1)u_1^{(2)}(x_1, 0) \tag{13.10}$

The boundary value problems for the functions $u_1^{(1)} - iu_2^{(1)}, u_1^{(2)} - iu_2^{(2)}$, $u_1^{(3)} - iu_2^{(3)}$, which vanish at infinity and satisfy the boundary conditions given by (13.6)′, (13.7)′, (13.8)′ have, as is well known, the solutions

$$u_1^{(1)} - iu_2^{(1)} = +\frac{1}{\pi}\int_0^1 \frac{F'(w)}{z-w}\,dw \tag{13.11}$$

$$u_1^{(2)} - iu_2^{(2)} = +\frac{1}{\pi}\int_0^1 \frac{G'(w)}{z-w}\,dw \tag{13.12}$$

and $\qquad u_1^{(3)} - iu_2^{(3)} = +\frac{1}{\pi}\int_0^1 \frac{H'(w)}{z-w}\,dw \tag{13.13}$

where in each integration we take the *Cauchy principal value* of the integral when necessary.

We now examine the behavior of $F'(x_1)$, $G'(x_1)$ and $H'(x_1)$ in the neighborhood of the origin. From equation (13.1) we find that near $x_1 = 0$

$$F(x_1) \sim x_1^{\frac{1}{2}} F_0 \tag{13.14}$$

$$F'(x_1) \sim \tfrac{1}{2} x_1^{-\frac{1}{2}} F_0 \tag{13.15}$$

$$F''(x_1) \sim -\tfrac{1}{4} x_1^{-\frac{3}{2}} F_0 \tag{13.16}$$

hence, using equations (13.9) and (13.10),

$$G'(x_1) \sim F'(x_1) \sim \tfrac{1}{2} x_1^{-\frac{1}{2}} F_0 \tag{13.17}$$

$$H'(x_1) \sim \tfrac{1}{2} F F' F'' \sim \tfrac{1}{16} x_1^{-\frac{3}{2}} F_0^3 \tag{13.18}$$

$(u_1^{(1)}(x_1, 0)$ and $u_1^{(2)}(x_1, 0)$ are bounded near $x_1 = 0)$.

At this stage it is possible to see how the perturbation procedure has broken down. Consider, for example, the expansion for u_2 when $x_2 = +0$. We see, from (13.6)', (13.7)', (13.8)' and (13.17), (13.18), that although the ratio of $\varepsilon^2 u_2^{(2)}$ to $\varepsilon u_2^{(1)}$ is $0(\varepsilon)$, the ratio of $\varepsilon^3 u_2^{(3)}$ to $\varepsilon^2 u_2^{(2)}$ is like ε/x_1; hence, the expansion is not valid near $x_1 = 0$ since the ratio of successive terms is not small. Clearly, then, since the process diverges near $x_1 = 0$, the first term would be of no value there. A general technique for correcting small-parameter expansions which fail in this way has been described by Lighthill.[1] The method is to expand the dependent variables *and* independent variables (although it may only be necessary to change one of them) in powers of ε where the coefficients are functions of new independent variables; the additional functions appearing in this way are then chosen to insure that the process does not diverge as it did originally.

In our case the following expansions, with a new variable X, are required:

$$u_1 = U_1^\infty \{ 1 + \varepsilon u_1^{(1)}(X, x_2) + \varepsilon^2 u_2^{(2)}(X, x_2) + ... \}$$

$$u_2 = U_1^\infty \{ \varepsilon u_2^{(1)}(X, x_2) + \varepsilon^2 u_2^{(2)}(X, x_2) + ... \} \tag{13.19}$$

$$x_1 = X + \lambda \varepsilon^2 + ...$$

where it is sufficient to take λ constant. λ will now be chosen so that $u_1^{(3)}$ and $u_2^{(3)}$ remain of the same order as $u_1^{(2)}$, $u_2^{(2)}$ and $u_1^{(1)}$, $u_2^{(1)}$; to ensure that $u_1^{(4)}, u_2^{(4)}$ are of the same order, further terms in x_1 must be considered but we shall not do this.

[1] "A technique for rendering approximate solutions to physical problems uniformly valid", *Phil. Mag.*, Vol. 40, pp. 1179–1201 (1949).

In terms of the new variables $X + ix_2$ we have that equation (13.3) remains the same, furthermore the conditions at infinity remain unchanged (i.e. $u_j^{(i)} = 0$ at infinity); however, the boundary conditions (13.6)–(13.10) are modified. They can be rederived starting from the condition of sliding, in terms of the new variable; this condition is,

$$u_2/u_1 = \pm \varepsilon F'(X + \lambda \varepsilon^2) \quad \text{on } x_2 = \pm \varepsilon F(X + \lambda \varepsilon^2) \qquad (13.20)$$

To obtain the conditions $u_1^{(i)}, u_2^{(i)}$ for $i = 1, 2, 3$, we equate the coefficients of the first three powers of ε, in (13.20). Up to this order, (13.20) may be written

$$u_2/u_1 = \pm \{\varepsilon F'(X) + \lambda \varepsilon^3 F''(X) + ...\} \quad \text{on } x_2 = \pm \varepsilon F(X) \quad (13.21)$$

(since u_2/u_1 is $0(\varepsilon)$ and the change in the value of x_2 is $0(\varepsilon^3)$, the resulting change on the left hand side is $0(\varepsilon^4)$). Therefore, since expansions u_1 and u_2 are the same as (13.4) with X replacing x_1, the boundary condition gives

$$u_1^{(1)}(X, \pm 0) = \pm F'(X)$$
$$u_2^{(2)}(X, \pm 0) = \pm G'(X)$$

with $G(X) = u_1^{(1)}(X, 0)F(X)$. Hence the solutions $u_1^{(1)}, u_2^{(2)}$ and $u_1^{(2)}, u_2^{(2)}$ are exactly as before (13.11) and (13.12) but with x_1 replaced by X. However the condition on $u_3^{(2)}$ is modified by the additional term $\lambda \varepsilon^3 F''(X)$ on the right hand side of (13.21); it is

$$u_2^{(3)}(X, \pm 0) = \pm H'(X)$$

where, now

$$H(X) = u_1^{(2)}(X, 0)F(X) + \tfrac{1}{2}F^2(X)F''(X) + \lambda F'(X)$$

For small X, $F(X)$ and $G(X)$ are $0(X^{\frac{1}{2}})$ and $H(X) \equiv (\tfrac{1}{2}\lambda F_0 - \tfrac{1}{8}F_0^3)X^{-\frac{1}{2}} + + 0(X^{\frac{1}{2}})$. In order to retain the validity of the expansion scheme (13.19) for small X, F, G and H must be of the same order; therefore, we choose

$$\lambda = \tfrac{1}{4}F_0^2$$

Of course the functions $u_2^{(i)}$ have a singularity at $X = 0, x_2 = 0$ but this does not matter because this point which is $x_1 = \tfrac{1}{4}F_0^2 \varepsilon^2, x_2 = 0$, is inside the airfoil and is not in the flow region. The expansions are valid in the fluid near and at the leading edge $x_1 = x_2 = 0$, since although the $u_2^{(i)}$ are large like ε^{-1}, the ratio of successive terms in u_2 is still $0(\varepsilon)$.

4 STFD

Although it was necessary to go to higher terms to correct the theory, we would usually be satisfied with the expansions (13.19) up to the second order. To this approximation, the result is simply: *in the results of the usual thin airfoil theory*, (13.11) *and* (13.12), *replace* x_1 *by* $x_1 - \frac{1}{4}F_0^2 \varepsilon^2$. Thus the first uniformly valid approximation is

$$u_1 - iu_2 = U_1^\infty + \frac{\varepsilon U_1^\infty}{\pi} \int_0^1 \frac{F'(w)\,dw}{x_1 - \frac{1}{4}F_0^2 \varepsilon^2 + ix_2 - w} \tag{13.22}$$

It may be noted that the radius of curvature of the airfoil of the leading edge $\rho_L = \frac{1}{2}\varepsilon^2 F_0^2$ so that the change in x_1 coordinate is $\frac{1}{2}\rho$.

To verify that the correct behavior near the leading edge has actually been obtained, we remark that

$$\frac{1}{\pi} \int_0^1 \frac{F'(w)\,dw}{z-w} \sim \frac{-iF_0}{2z^{\frac{1}{2}}}$$

near $z = 0$. Hence, (13.22) gives

$$u_1 - iu_2 \sim U_1^\infty - \frac{\frac{1}{2}iF_0 \varepsilon U_1^\infty}{\{x_1 - \frac{1}{4}\varepsilon^2 F_0^2 + ix_2\}^{\frac{1}{2}}}$$

near the leading edge; at $x_1 = x_2 = 0$, the second term becomes $-U_1^\infty$ so that the leading edge is indeed a stagnation point. Near the origin

$$\frac{1}{\pi} \int_0^1 \frac{F'(w)\,dw}{z-w}\,dw \sim -\frac{iF_0}{2z^{\frac{1}{2}}}$$

as may easily be checked since

$$\frac{1}{\pi} \int_0^1 \frac{F'(w)}{z-w}\,dw = +\frac{F_0}{2\pi z^{\frac{1}{2}}} \int_0^{z\infty} \frac{dw}{w^{\frac{1}{2}}(1-w)} + \text{bounded part}$$

The same procedure can be applied successfully in determining the flow about an unsymmetrical airfoil at incidence of $\varepsilon\alpha$. To this end we suppose that $u_1 = U_1^\infty \cos\alpha\varepsilon, u_2 = U_1^\infty \sin\alpha\varepsilon$ at infinity while the airfoil is supposed to be given by

$$x_2 = \varepsilon[C(x_1) \pm F(x_1)]; \qquad 0 \leq x_1 \leq 1$$

The boundary condition on the airfoil is

$$u_2/u_1 = \varepsilon[C'(x) \pm F'(x)]$$

For the straightforward expansion (13.4), $u_1^{(1)}$ and $u_2^{(1)}$ satisfy the equations of motion (13.1), the boundary condition

$$u_2^{(1)}(x_1, \pm 0) = C'(x_1) \pm F'(x_1)$$

and the condition $u_1^{(1)} = 0$, $u_2^{(1)} = \alpha$ at infinity

The solution to this boundary value problem is

$$u_1^{(1)} - iu_2^{(1)} = \frac{1}{\pi} \int_0^1 \frac{F'(w)\,dw}{x_1 + ix_2 - w}$$
$$+ \left(\frac{1 - x_1 - ix_2}{x_1 + ix_2}\right)^{\frac{1}{2}} \left\{\alpha + \frac{1}{\pi} \int_0^1 \frac{C'(w)}{x_1 + ix_2 - w} \cdot \left(\frac{w}{1-w}\right)^{\frac{1}{2}} dw\right\} \tag{13.23}$$

A detailed investigation of the perturbation procedure shows that exactly the same modifications are necessary: to obtain a uniformly valid solution x_1 must be replaced everywhere in (13.23) by

$$x_1 - \tfrac{1}{4}F_0^2\,\varepsilon^2 = x_1 - \tfrac{1}{2}\rho_L$$

CHAPTER 14

Airfoil of Finite Span[1]

The problems considered so far referred to two-dimensional flows past airfoils of infinite span. We now proceed to discuss the flow induced by an airfoil of finite span assuming that the airfoil moves with constant velocity. We do not consider the case in which the motion begins at a finite time. We consider only the case of the flow that results asymptotically as the time tends to infinity. The vortex sheet which leaves the trailing edge therefore does not have a finite front edge but extends to infinity. Furthermore, the flow then is steady when observed from the airfoil.

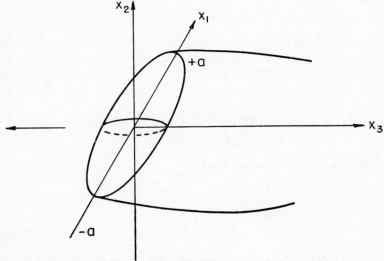

Fig. 14.1.

[1] For the history of this theory see the article by Giacomelli and Pistolesi in *Durant Aerodynamic Theory*, Vol. I, pp. 305 ff.

89

We place the x_1-axis, instead of the x_3-axis, along the span of the airfoil (see Fig. 4.1). The airfoil is then described by

$$x_2 = y^{\pm}(x_1, x_3) \tag{14.1}$$

the functions $x_3^{\pm}$ are defined on the base of the airfoil

$$\mathscr{A}: \qquad x_3^-(x_1) \leqq x_3 \leqq x_3^+(x_1)$$

The functions $x_3^{\pm}(x_1)$ are defined for $-a \leqq x_1 \leqq a$, so that $2a$ is the span of the airfoil. *Note that the functions $y^{\pm}$ are independent of the time t.*

The velocity of the relative flow at infinity will be assumed to have the direction of the positive x_3-axis,

$$U^{\infty} = \{0, 0, U_3^{\infty}\}, \qquad U_3^{\infty} > 0 \tag{14.2}$$

As before, the velocity of the absolute flow will be denoted by u, so that $U^{\infty} + u$ is the velocity of the steady relative flow. The velocity u, considered as a function of x, is then independent of the time. The potential of the absolute flow is ϕ, as before, and $(U^{\infty}x) + \phi$ is the potential of the relative flow. Evidently

$$u = \nabla\phi \tag{14.3}$$

We adopt the approximation which was developed in chapter 8 under the assumption that the airfoil is flat. We then seek a potential function $\phi(x)$ which satisfies the conditions of sliding on the airfoil and the vortex sheet together with the condition of pressure equality on both sides of the vortex sheet.

The condition of sliding for the base of the airfoil is

$$u_2^{\pm}(x_1, x_3) = U_3^{\infty} \nabla_3 \, y^{\pm}(x_1, x_3) \quad \text{on } \mathscr{A} \tag{14.4}$$

On the base $\mathscr{S}$ of the vortex sheet

$$\mathscr{S}: \qquad x_3^{\pm}(x_1) \leqq x_3, \qquad -a \leqq x_1 \leqq a$$

the condition of sliding is

$$u_2^{\pm} = U_3^{\infty} \nabla_3 \, y; \tag{14.5}$$

here the function $y(x_1, x_3)$ is unknown. We eliminate the latter condition by forming the jump

$$\hat{u}_2 = 0 \quad \text{on } \mathscr{S} \tag{14.6}$$

The condition of pressure equality on the vortex sheet reduces to

$$\hat{u}_3 = 0 \quad \text{on } \mathscr{S} \tag{14.7}$$

in the present approximation as follows from Bernoulli's law, cf. (2.7). Furthermore, the vector γ defined by (5.2)

$$\gamma = n_2 \{0, 0, \hat{u}_1\} \tag{14.8}$$

has the direction of the main stream. The vortex lines, therefore, are the lines $x_1 = \text{const.}$ and $x_2 = \text{const.}$; they lead from the trailing edge to infinity.

Conditions (14.6) and (14.7) are equivalent with the condition that a function $\Gamma(x_1)$ exists such that

$$\hat{\phi} = \Gamma(x_1) \quad \text{on } \mathscr{S} \tag{14.9}$$

In other words, the jump of potential is constant along the vortex lines $x_1 = \text{const.}$ on the vortex sheet. Since the jump $\hat{\phi}$ is the circulation of a contour connecting the lower with the upper sides of the vortex sheet at $\{x_1, 0, x_3\}$ we see that $\Gamma(x_1)$ is the circulation around the profile on a contour which leads from the point $\{x_1, 0, x_3^+ (x_1)\}$ on the trailing edge on the lower side around the airfoil to the same point on the upper side of the airfoil. Incidentally, this circulation corresponds to the "counter circulation" in two-dimensional flow since there the circulation is usually referred to a circuit which goes from the upper to the lower side.

We observe that condition (14.9) implies that $\hat{\phi}$ does not approach zero as $x_3 \to +\infty$. As to the behavior of $\hat{\phi}$ at infinity we must confine ourselves to requiring that ϕ approaches zero if $x_3 \to -\infty$ and $x_1^2 + x_3^2 \to \infty$. (More precisely we may require that $\phi - \phi^{(s)} \to 0$ for $|x| \to \infty$ where $\phi^{(s)}$ is the special double layer potential described below.)

The value of the circulation $\Gamma(x_1)$ should be so determined that the Kutta condition is satisfied at the trailing edge. If this circulation were known one could find the potential ϕ as follows. First, one determines a function $\phi^{(s)}(x)$ which satisfies the condition

$$\hat{\phi}^{(s)}(x) = \Gamma(x_1) \qquad \widehat{\nabla_2 \phi}^{(s)} = 0 \text{ on } \mathscr{S}$$

This can be done explicitly, as we shall show below, by considering $\Gamma(x_1)$ as a double layer "charge" distribution. Then the function $\phi^{(p)} = \phi - \phi^{(s)}$ can be found as the potential function satisfying the condition

$$\nabla_2 \phi^{(p)} = -\nabla_2 \phi^{(s)} + U_3^\infty \nabla_3 y^\pm$$

on the two sides of $\mathscr{A}$, which is equivalent with (14.4); further $\phi^{(p)}$ should be regular on the sheet $\mathscr{S}$ and vanish at infinity. The problem of finding $\phi^{(p)}$ is a special case of the second boundary value problem of potential theory. The determination of $\phi^{(p)}$ can therefore be reduced to an integral equation for a single layer charge distribution on each side of $\mathscr{A}$. The result still depends on the choice of the function $\Gamma(x_1)$. The Kutta condition then leads to an integral equation for the determination of this circulation function.

Wing as Vortex Line

In the following we shall confine ourselves to treating the limiting case in which the airfoil has shrunk to a vortex line; specifically, to the vortex line

$$\mathscr{L}: \qquad x_3 = 0, \qquad x_2 = 0, \qquad -a \leqq x_1 \leqq a$$

Each point of this line carries a circulation $\Gamma(x_1)$. We first take the attitude that this circulation function is known. Later on we shall discuss the question of how to determine this circulation function from the shape of the given profile before it shrinks to a point.

The potential function of the problem now considered is completely determined by the jump $\hat{\phi} = \Gamma(x_1)$ of the potential on the base $\mathscr{S}$ of the vortex sheet. The fact that this jump does not vanish at the edge $\mathscr{L}$ of the base $\mathscr{S}$ insures that the flow has the proper singularity on this line. The jump of the potential ϕ on a surface is exactly the double layer charge there.

Since the jump of the normal derivative of ϕ is zero on this surface, according to condition (14.6), the potential ϕ can be given explicitly

$$\phi(x) = -\frac{1}{4\pi} \int_{\mathscr{S}} \int \Gamma(x_1') \nabla_2 \, |\, x - x' \,|^{-1} \, dx_1' \, dx_3' \qquad (14.10)$$

The validity of this formula can be ascertained in the well-known manner by Green's formula (cf. O. D. Kellog: *Potential Theory*).

CHAPTER 15

Discussion of the Velocity Field of a Flow past an Airfoil of Finite Span

We proceed to discuss the velocity field associated with the potential (14.10). From the behavior of the velocity at infinity we shall be able to derive the forces acting on the airfoil. Furthermore, the knowledge of the velocity field at the vortex line $x_2 = x_3 = 0$ will enable us to determine the circulation produced by an airfoil with a given profile.

For the following considerations it is convenient to write

$$\phi(x) = \nabla_2 \Phi(x) \tag{15.1}$$

with
$$\Phi(x) = -\frac{1}{4\pi} \int_{\mathscr{S}} \Gamma(x_1') \left| |x'-x|^{-1} - b(x_3') \right| dx_1' \, dx_3' \tag{15.2}$$

where
$$b(x_3') = \frac{1}{\sqrt{((x_3')^2+1)}}$$

Note that in order to make the integrand of (15.2) integrable it is necessary to subtract the function $b(x_3')$ or any other appropriate function making the integrand of (15.2) integrable. Since the jump $+\Gamma(x_1)$ of ϕ depends only on x_1 we may carry out the integration with respect to x_3' in (15.2). Because of

$$|x'-x|^{-1} - b(x_3') = \nabla_3' \log \frac{|x'-x|+x_3'-x_3}{\sqrt{((x_3')^2+1)}+x_3'}$$

and
$$\frac{|x'-x|+x_3'-x_3}{\sqrt{((x_3')^2+1)}+x_3'} \to 1 \quad \text{as } x_3' \to \infty$$

we find
$$\Phi(x) = \frac{1}{4\pi} \int_{-a}^{+a} \Gamma(x_1') \log \left[|x'-x|-x_3 \right] dx_1' \tag{15.3}$$

93

and hence using (15.1)

$$\phi(x) = \frac{1}{4\pi} \int_{-a}^{+a} \Gamma(x_1') \frac{1}{|x_1'-x|-x_3} \frac{x_2}{|x'-x|} dx_1' \tag{15.4}$$

We first investigate the behavior of $\phi(x)$ and $u(x) = \nabla\phi(x)$ for large $|x|$. This behavior depends on the manner in which $|x|$ tends to infinity. Suppose first that x_3 remains less than a bound c while $|x| \to \infty$. In this case $|x'-x| - x_3 \to \infty$ as $|x| \to \infty$ and hence we may conclude from (15.4) that

$$\phi(x) \to 0, \qquad 0\left(\frac{1}{|x|}\right) \tag{15.5}$$

$$\text{as } |x| \to \infty \quad \text{while } x_3 \leqq c$$

$$u(x) \to 0, \qquad 0\left(\frac{1}{|x|^2}\right) \tag{15.6}$$

Secondly we assume that x_3 becomes positive infinite while x_1 and x_2 remain constant. Then, recalling that $|x'-x| = \sqrt{((x_1'-x_1)^2 + x_2^2 + x_3^2)}$, we have

$$\frac{1}{|x'-x|-x_3} \cdot \frac{x_2}{|x'-x|} = \frac{|x'-x|+x_3}{|x'-x|^2 - x_3^2} \cdot \frac{x_2}{|x'-x|} \to \frac{2x_2}{(x_1'-x_1)^2 + x_2^2}$$

and consequently,

$$\phi(x) \to \phi^\infty(x) \quad \text{as } x_3 \to +\infty, \qquad x_1, x_2 \text{ const.} \tag{15.7}$$

with
$$\phi^\infty(x) = \frac{1}{2\pi} \int_{-a}^{+a} \Gamma(x_1') \frac{x_2}{(x_1'-x_1)^2 + x_2^2} dx_1' \tag{15.8}$$

This relation implies that $u_3(x) \to 0$ as $x_3 \to \infty$ so that more generally we have

$$u_3(x) \to 0 \quad \text{as } |x| \to \infty \tag{15.9}$$

For later purposes it is important to evaluate the limit which the velocity component $u_2^{(\infty)} = \nabla_2 \phi^\infty$ approaches as x_2 approaches zero. We first note that $\phi^\infty(x)$ is the real part of the analytic function

$$\chi^\infty(z) = \frac{1}{2\pi i} \int_{-a}^{+a} \Gamma(x_1') \frac{dx_1'}{x_1'-z} \tag{15.10}$$

of the complex variable $z = x_1 + ix_2$ since

$$\text{Im}\frac{1}{x_1'-z} = \frac{\text{Im}(x_1'-\bar{z})}{(x_1'-x_1)^2+x_2^2} = \frac{x_2}{(x_1'-x_1)^2+x_2^2}$$

Through integration by parts in (15.10) we find, recalling that $\Gamma(x_1')$ vanishes at the end points $\pm a$, that

$$\chi^{\infty}(z) = -\frac{1}{2\pi i}\int_{-a}^{+a} \nabla_1' \Gamma(x_1')\log(x_1'-z)\,dx_1' \tag{15.11}$$

from which we obtain

$$\bar{w}^{\infty}(z) = \frac{d}{dz}\chi^{\infty}(z)$$

$$= -\frac{1}{2\pi i}\frac{d}{dz}\left\{\int_{-a}^{+a} \nabla_1' \Gamma(x_1')\log(x_1'-z)\,dx_1'\right\} \tag{15.12}$$

In the latter relation we may carry out the operation of differentiation under the integral sign if we take Cauchy's principal value of the resulting integral (cf. e.g. Mihlin, *Singular Integral Equations*, Russian translation No. 24, A.M.S.). We thus obtain from (15.12)

$$\bar{w}^{\infty}(z) = +\frac{1}{2\pi i}\int_{-a}^{+a} \nabla_1' \Gamma(x_1')\frac{dx_1'}{x_1'-z} \tag{15.13}$$

As $x_2 \to 0$, the negative imaginary part, $u_2^{\infty}(x_1, x_2)$, of this expression approaches the expression

$$u_2^{\infty}(x_1, 0) = \frac{1}{2\pi}\int_{-a}^{+a} \nabla_1' \Gamma(x_1')\frac{dx_1'}{x_1'-x_1} \tag{15.14}$$

in which the integral is understood to be taken as Cauchy's principal value. We note that the velocity u_2^{∞} has no jump at the slit $x_2 = 0$, $|x_1| \leq a$, as is to be expected since u_2 has no such jump for finite values of x_3.

The fact that the flow quantities approach limits as $x_3 \to \infty$ is due to the approximation that was made. The actual vortex sheet does not remain on the plane $x_2 = 0$ but slopes downward as will be shown below. Limits of the flow quantities which are different from zero are probably attained if one moves to infinity in an appropriate direction.

For the description of the *flow near the vortex line* $x_3 = 0$ it is convenient to introduce the functions

$$\psi_1(x) = -\nabla_3 \Phi, \qquad \psi_3(x) = \nabla_1 \Phi \qquad (15.15)$$

as the components of the vector

$$\psi(x) = \{\psi_1(x), 0, \psi_3(x)\} \qquad (15.16)$$

From the fact that the function Φ, given by (15.3), satisfies the equation

$$\nabla^2 \Phi = 0$$

together with (15.1) and (14.3), one verifies that the curl of the vector $\psi(x)$ is the velocity

$$u(x) = [\nabla, \psi(x)] \qquad (15.17)$$

Using (15.15) one also verifies the relation

$$(\nabla \psi) = 0$$

Thus $\psi(x)$ is recognized to be the stream vector introduced in chapter 2.

Carrying out the differentiation $-\nabla_3$ on the function Φ given by (15.3) we find

$$\psi_1(x) = \frac{1}{4\pi} \int_{-a}^{+a} \Gamma(x_1') \frac{dx_1'}{|x'-x|} \qquad (15.18)$$

where we imply $x_2' = x_3' = 0$.

The contribution to the velocity due to this component $\psi_1(x)$ may be ascribed to a distribution of circulation along the line $x_2' = x_3' = 0$, $|x_1'| \leqq a$. The contribution due to the component $\psi_3(x)$ may similarly be ascribed to a distribution of vorticity on the base of the vortex sheet. As a matter of fact the expression for $u(x)$ which results after insertion of $\psi_1(x)$ and $\psi_3(x)$ in (15.17) could be derived from Biot-Savart's law, cf. (2.28).

In order to obtain ψ_3 we carry out the differentiation ∇_1 then set $\nabla_1 = -\nabla_1'$ on the function Φ given by (15.3), and integrate by parts; thus we find

$$\psi_3(x) = \frac{1}{4\pi} \int_{-a}^{+a} \nabla_1' \Gamma(x_1') \cdot \log[|x'-x| - x_3] \, dx_1' \qquad (15.19)$$

since $\Gamma(x_1') = 0$ for $x_1' = \pm a$, here we set $x_1' = x_3' = 0$ in the integrand.

The contributions to the velocity which are due to the components ψ_1 and ψ_3 will be denoted by $u^{(1)}$ and $u^{(3)}$ respectively. Thus

$$u = u^{(1)} + u^{(3)} \tag{15.20}$$

where
$$u^{(1)} = \{0, u_2^{(1)}, u_3^{(1)}\} \tag{15.21}$$

with
$$u_2^{(1)} = \nabla_3 \psi_1, \qquad u_3^{(1)} = -\nabla_2 \psi_1 \tag{15.22}$$

and
$$u^{(3)} = \{u_1^{(3)}, u_2^{(3)}, 0\} \tag{15.23}$$

with
$$u_1^{(3)} = \nabla_2 \psi_3, \qquad u_2^{(3)} = -\nabla_1 \psi_3 \tag{15.24}$$

We shall first investigate the behavior of $u^{(3)}$ near the vortex line. The behavior of $u_1^{(3)}(x)$ near the vortex line is given by

$$u_1^{(3)}(x) \sim +\frac{1}{2\pi} \nabla_1 \Gamma(x_1) \arctan\left(-\frac{x_2}{x_3}\right), \qquad x_2^2 + x_3^2 \sim 0 \tag{15.25}$$

We do not give the details of the calculation here. We only observe that this component changes from the value $-\frac{1}{2}\nabla_1 \Gamma(x_1)$ to the value $\frac{1}{2}\nabla_1 \Gamma(x_1)$ on a circuit which starts at a point near $(x_1, 0, 0)$ on the lower side of the sheet to the same point on the upper side. This is in agreement with the fact that the velocity component has the jump $\nabla_1 \Gamma(x_1)$ at the sheet.

For the calculation $u_2^{(3)}$ at the vortex line we may first set $x_2 = x_3 = 0$ and then differentiate ψ_3 with respect to x_1. We obtain from (15.19), upon setting $x_2 = x_3 = 0$,

$$\psi_3(x_1) = \frac{1}{4\pi} \int_{-a}^{+a} \nabla_1' \Gamma(x_1') \cdot \log|x_1' - x_1| \, dx_1', \qquad x_2 = x_3 = 0 \tag{15.26}$$

We notice that under very general assumptions on $\nabla_1' \Gamma(x_1')$ the integrand of (14.23) is integrable, e.g. if $\nabla_1' \Gamma(x_1')$ is continuous. As before, we may differentiate the right member of (15.26) under the integral sign if we take Cauchy's principal value of the resulting integral.

The component $u_2^{(3)}$ of the velocity is then found to be

$$u_2^{(3)}(x) = \frac{1}{4\pi} \int_{-a}^{+a} \nabla_1' \Gamma(x_1') \frac{dx_1'}{x_1' - x_1} \qquad x = \{x_1, 0, 0\} \tag{15.27}$$

By comparison with formula (15.14) we see that this velocity component is one half of the corresponding velocity component u_2^∞ at infinity, i.e. as $x_3 \to \infty$.

The velocity component $u_2^{(3)}$ will in general be negative since in general $\nabla_1 \Gamma(x_1) \lessgtr 0$ for $x_1 \gtrless 0$ and for this reason it is called the "downwash velocity". *The occurrence of this downwash velocity is the most significant effect of the finiteness of the span of the airfoil.*

An important conclusion can be drawn from this result: Because of condition (14.5), the negative sign of the velocity $u_2^{(3)}$ implies that *the vortex sheet slopes downward from the trailing edge on.*

In order to determine the contribution $u^{(1)}(x)$ due to the component $\psi_1(x)$, cf. (15.21), and hence to the distribution of circulation on the vortex line we apply integration by parts to formula (15.13) separately for $-a \leqq x_1' \leqq x_1$ and for $x_1 \leqq x_1' \leqq a$. We obtain

$$\psi_1(x) = \frac{1}{4\pi} \int_{-a}^{+a} \nabla_1' \Gamma(x_1') \operatorname{sgn}(x_1 - x_1') \log\left[|x' - x| + |x_1' - x_1| \right] dx_1'$$
$$- \frac{1}{4\pi} \Gamma(x_1) \log(x_2^2 + x_3^2) \tag{15.28}$$

We may not set $x_2 = x_3 = 0$ in the last term of (15.28), but we may do so in the first term since the resulting term is finite. Since this term is then independent of x_2 and x_3 it does not contribute to $u^{(1)}(x)$. Accordingly, we obtain approximately

$$u^{(1)}(x) \sim \frac{1}{2\pi} \Gamma(x_1) \left\{ 0, -\frac{x_3}{x_2^2 + x_3^2}, \frac{x_2}{x_2^2 + x_3^2} \right\} \tag{15.29}$$

Evidently, *the* approximate *velocity field* $u^{(1)}(x)$ *is the one that would result if the whole axis carried the constant circulation* $\Gamma(x_1)$.

The *potential* associated with the velocity field just described can be easily determined from (15.29), (15.25), (15.27). We find

$$\phi(x) \sim \frac{1}{2\pi} \Gamma(x_1) \arctan\left(-\frac{x_2}{x_3} \right) + x_2 u_2^{(3)}(x_1, 0, 0) \tag{15.30}$$

except possibly for an additive constant. As we can easily see, differentiation with respect to x_2 and x_3 of the first term here leads to the velocity $u^{(1)}(x)$, cf. (15.29); differentiation of this term with respect to x_1 leads to the contribution to $u^{(3)}(x)$ given by (15.25). Differentiation of the last term in (15.30) with respect to x_2 leads to the downwash contribution (15.27) to $u^{(3)}(x)$. Differentiation of the last term of (15.30) with respect to x_1 yields an additional term not occurring in $u^{(1)}(x) + u^{(3)}(x)$. However since this last term is multiplied by x_2 it is small near the vortex filament so that it may be considered of higher order and, therefore, neglected. The velocity field which we have discussed describes the actual velocity field only to the first order. The actual flow differs in many respects from the first order flow. We have already seen

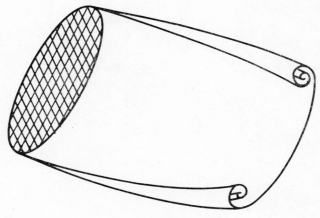

Fig. 15.1.

that the vortex sheet slopes downward. In addition, it is claimed, and probably true for stationary airfoils, that the edges of the vortex sheet curl upwards as indicated in the figure above. Whether or not the cross-section through the vortex sheet approaches a definite shape at infinity and what this shape is seems to be unknown. Naturally it would be of great interest if this could be determined.

CHAPTER 16

Forces Acting on Airfoil of Finite Span

In order to evaluate the force $F = \{F_1, F_2, F_3\}$ exerted by the fluid on the airfoil we determine the resultant of the pressure forces acting on, and the momentum flux into, a *test surface* $\mathcal{T}$ enclosing their foil at great distances; see chapter 1, p. 5. At points very far from the airfoil, our flow is no longer an approximation to the actual flow since the deviation of the true vortex sheet from the plane half strip increases with distance. This deviation, however, is small near the airfoil so that the forces on the airfoil are approximately those exerted by the approximate flow *at the airfoil*. The calculation of the latter forces by means of an infinitely far removed test surface is a mathematical device involving only this approximate flow. It is therefore independent of whether or not this flow is an approximation to the actual flow on the test surface.

As test surface $\mathcal{T}$ we choose the parallelopiped with faces $x_1 = \pm b_1$, $x_2 = \pm b_2, x_3 = \pm b_3$. For simplicity we assume that the airfoil is symmetric so that $\Gamma(-x_1) = \Gamma(x_1)$. As a consequence, clearly, the x_1-component F_1 of the force is zero. It could be shown, though, that this is true for general airfoils without symmetry. To calculate the x_3-component F_3 we make use of Bernoulli's law. Since $U^\infty + u$ is the velocity of the flow, Bernoulli's law becomes

$$p = -\frac{\rho}{2} |U^\infty + u|^2 + \text{const.} \tag{16.1}$$

Further $(U^\infty n + un)$ is the outward normal component of this velocity on $\mathcal{T}$ and hence $\rho(U_3^\infty + u_3)(U^\infty n + un)$ is the x_3-component of the momentum flux out of $\mathcal{T}$. Hence we obtain for the x_3-component of the force

$$F_3 = \tfrac{1}{2}\rho \int \{|U^\infty + u|^2 n_3 - 2(U^\infty n + un)(U_3^\infty + u_3)\} \, dT \tag{16.2}$$

101

Since the total flux of mass across $\mathscr{T}$ is zero,

$$\int_{\mathscr{T}} (U^\infty + u)n \, dT = 0$$

relation (16.2) reduces to

$$F_3 = \tfrac{1}{2}\rho \int_{\mathscr{T}} \{|U^\infty + u|^2 n_3 - 2(U^\infty n + un)u_3\} \, dT \qquad (16.3)$$

From $\qquad |U^\infty + u|^2 = |U_3^\infty|^2 + 2U_3^\infty u_3 + u_1^2 + u_2^2 + u_3^2 \qquad (16.4)$

and $(U^\infty n) = U_3^\infty n_3$ we find that the first order terms in the last expression for F_3 cancel. In view of $\int_{\mathscr{T}} (U_3^\infty)^2 n_3 dT = 0$ this leaves

$$F_3 = \tfrac{1}{2}\rho \int_{\mathscr{T}} \{(u_1^2 + u_2^2 - u_3^2)n_3 - 2u_1 u_3 n_1 - 2u_2 u_3 n_2\} \, dT \quad (16.5)$$

We now remove first the faces $x_3 = \pm b_3$ by letting $b_3 \to \infty$ with the result

$$F_3 = \tfrac{1}{2}\rho \int_{\mathscr{T}} \{(u_1^2 + u_2^2)n_3 - 2u_1 u_3 n_1 - 2u_2 u_3 n_2\} \, dT \qquad (16.6)$$

since $u_3 \to 0$ as $|x_3| \to \infty$ by (15.9). Secondly, we remove the other faces by letting b_1 and b_2 tend to infinity. From (15.6) it is seen that the result is

$$F_3 = \tfrac{1}{2}\rho \iint_{\mathscr{P}_\infty} (u_1^\infty)^2 + (u_2^\infty)^2 \, dx_1 \, dx_2 \qquad (16.7)$$

where u_1^∞ and u_2^∞ are the limit values of the velocity components u_2 and u_3 for $x_3 \to \infty$ cf. (15.13) and the integration refers to the complete (x_1, x_2)-plane $\mathscr{P}_\infty$.

To evaluate the x_2-component of the force we write

$$F_2 = \tfrac{1}{2}\rho \int_{\mathscr{T}} \{|U^\infty + u|^2 n_2 - 2(U^\infty n + un)u_2\} \, dT \qquad (16.8)$$

in analogy with (16.2). To within second order terms this becomes

$$F_2 = \rho u_3 \int_{\mathscr{T}} (u_3 n_2 - u_2 n_3) \, dT \qquad (16.9)$$

or, as one readily verifies

$$F_2 = \rho U_3^\infty \int_{-b_1}^{b_1} \left(\oint_{\mathscr{C}(x_1)} d\phi \right) dx_1 \qquad (16.10)$$

Here ϕ is the velocity potential and the circuit $\mathscr{C}(x_1)$ runs on the intersection of the plane $x_1 = $ const. with the test surface from the lower to the upper point of intersection with test surface $\mathscr{T}$ and the sheet. The integral on $\mathscr{C}(x_1)$ is exactly the circulation $\Gamma(x_1)$ for $|x_1| \leqq a$ and zero for $|x_1| > a$. Thus we have the result

$$F_2 = \rho U_3^\infty \int_{-a}^{+a} \Gamma(x_1) \, dx_1 \qquad (16.11)$$

This formula was derived after neglecting the terms of second order in u. Actually, the contribution of these terms is exactly zero. In order to show this one may first remove the faces $x_1 = \pm b_1$, $x_2 = \pm b_2$ and $x_3 = -b_3$ of the test surface to infinity. From the fact that the velocity $|u|$ dies out like $|x|^{-2}$ at infinity, provided $x_3 \leqq b_3$, cf. (15.6), one concludes that in the limit these faces give no contribution to the second order terms. The contribution of the face $x_3 = b$ is

$$-\rho \iint_{x_3 = b} u_3 u_2 \, dx_1 \, dx_2$$

as seen from (16.8). The velocity u_2 does not die out as $x_3 \to \infty$, but approaches a function which behaves like $c(x_1^2 + x_2^2)^{-1}$ at infinity while u_3 dies out like $|x|^{-2}$ as seen from (15.8). Consequently, the contribution from the face $x_3 = b_3$ also vanishes in the limit. Since the force F_2, given by (16.8), is independent of the choice of the test surface $\mathscr{T}$ and the expression (16.11) is also independent, it follows that the second order terms do not contribute and that the expression (16.11) is exact.

The expression for the lift F_2 is in complete agreement with the expression $\rho U_3^\infty \Gamma$ for the lift per unit length derived in Kutta and Joukowski theory. It is remarkable that in addition the fluid exerts a force F_3 in the direction of its velocity at infinity, this force is called the "induced drag". It is the main success of the theory of airfoils of finite span that it enables one to understand the origin of this drag.

CHAPTER 17

Airfoil of Minimum Drag

In the preceding chapter we have shown how to determine the lift and induced drag exerted on the airfoil once the distribution of circulation is known. The next problem would be to determine this distribution of circulation from the distribution of the shape and position of the airfoil. Before doing this, however, we shall try to find out which distribution of circulation, among all those that give the same lift, will minimize the induced drag. Actual airfoils will in general be so designed that the distribution of circulation which they produce does not differ much from the optimal one. Also it is to be noted that in the neighborhood of an extremal value the value of a function is very insensitive to changes of the independent variable. Therefore, the actual values of the induced drags will not differ much from the possible minimum value.

We make use of the possibility of expressing the lift and induced drag solely in terms of the flow in the plane $\mathscr{P}_\infty$ corresponding to $x_3 = \infty$. In the following the potential ϕ and the velocity $u = \nabla\phi = \{\nabla_1\phi, \nabla_2\phi\}$ refer to this flow. This potential, $\phi = \phi^\infty$, is given by formula (14.17),

$$\phi^\infty(x) = \frac{1}{2\pi}\int_{-a}^{+a}\Gamma(x_1')\frac{x_2}{(x_1'-x_1)^2+x_2^2}\,dx_1' \qquad (17.1)$$

We may read off from this formula that this potential ϕ behaves at infinity, i.e. as $x_1^2+x_2^2 \sim \infty$, like

$$\phi(x) \sim \frac{1}{2\pi}\frac{x_2}{x_1^2+x_2^2}\int_{-a}^{+a}\Gamma(x_1')\,dx_1' \qquad (17.2)$$

We also know that this potential has a jump

$$\hat{\phi} = \Gamma(x_1) \qquad (17.1)'$$

105

on the slit x_2, $|x_1| \leqq a$, while its normal derivative is continuous there,

$$\widehat{\nabla_2 \phi} = 0 \qquad (17.1)''$$

Formula (16.11) for the lift can therefore be written in the form

$$F_2 = \rho U_3^\infty \int_{-a}^{+a} \hat\phi(x_1, 0) \, dx_1 \qquad (17.3)$$

and formula (16.7) for the induced drag becomes

$$F_3 = \tfrac{1}{2}\rho \iint |\nabla \phi|^2 \, dx_1 \, dx_2 \qquad (17.4)$$

The problem is now to find a potential $\phi(x)$ having the behavior described by $(17.1)''$, $(17.1)'$ and leading to a given lift F_2 given by (17.3) for which the induced drag (17.4) is a minimum.

Suppose there is such a minimizing function $\phi_m(x)$. Then we consider another function of the same type,

$$\phi(x) = \phi_m(x) + \varepsilon \delta\phi(x), \qquad (17.5)$$

ε being an arbitrary parameter. Since both $\phi(x)$ and $\phi_m(x)$ are to satisfy condition (17.3) with the same value of F_2, the "variation" $\delta\phi(x)$ must satisfy the condition

$$\int_{-a}^{+a} \delta\hat\phi(x_1, 0) \, dx_1 = 0 \qquad (17.6)$$

Inserting $\phi_m + \varepsilon \delta\phi$ in the right member of (17.4) a quadratic function of ε results. This function has a minimum for $\varepsilon = 0$ since by assumption the drag F_3 has a smaller value for ϕ_m than for any other function ϕ. The condition that the derivative of the quadratic function vanishes for $\varepsilon = 0$ leads to the condition

$$\iint (\nabla\phi_m, \nabla\delta\phi) \, dx_1 \, dx_2 = 0 \qquad (17.7)$$

On the other hand, it is clear that a function $\phi_m(x)$ leading to the lift F_2 minimizes the drag F_3, whenever it satisfies condition (17.7).

We carry out integration by parts. Since $\nabla\phi_m$ vanishes like $c|x|^{-2}$ and $\delta\phi$ at least like $|x|^{-1}$ at infinity no contribution from infinity results. The contribution from the slit leads to

$$\int_{-a,\, x_2=0}^{+a} \nabla_2 \phi_m \widehat{\delta\phi} \, dx_1 = 0$$

Here we have made use of the fact that $\nabla_2 \phi_m$ has no jump at the slit, see (17.1)".

The continuous function $\delta\hat{\phi}(x_1)$ is quite arbitrary except for condition (17.6); for to every such function there belongs a flow potential $\delta\phi(x)$ according to (14.7). Let $\zeta(x_1)$ be any continuous function defined for $|x_1| \leqq a$. Then the function

$$\delta\hat{\phi}(x_1) = \zeta(x_1) - \frac{1}{2a}\int_{-a}^{+a} \zeta(x_1')\,dx_1'$$

satisfies condition (17.6). Consequently, by (17.8)

$$\int_{-a}^{+a} \nabla_2 \phi_m(x_1,0)\zeta(x_1)\,dx_1$$

or

$$-\frac{1}{2a}\int_{-a}^{+a} \nabla_2 \phi_m(x_1,0)\,dx_1 \int_{-a}^{+a} \zeta(x_1')\,dx_1' = 0$$

$$\int_{-a}^{+a}\left\{\nabla_2 \phi_m(x_1,0) - \frac{1}{2a}\int_{-a}^{+a} \nabla_2 \phi_m(x_1',0)\,dx_1'\right\}\zeta(x_1)\,dx_1 = 0$$

Since $\zeta(x_1)$ is arbitrary we may conclude that its factor vanishes, thus

$$\nabla_2 \phi_m(x_1,0) = \frac{1}{2a}\int_{-a}^{+a} \nabla_2 \phi_m(x_1',0)\,dx_1' \qquad (17.8)$$

The right hand side here is constant and thus we have derived the condition

$$\nabla_2 \phi_m(x_1,0) = \text{const.} \qquad (17.9)$$

Vice versa, if $\nabla_2 \phi_m(x_1,0)$ is constant relation (17.8) holds because of (17.6), hence (17.7) holds. The corresponding function $\phi_m(x)$ therefore minimizes the drag.

A flow potential for which the cross velocity $\nabla_2 \phi_m(x_1,0)$ is constant is well known; it is given by

$$\phi_m(x) = \omega \operatorname{Re}\pm\{\sqrt{(a^2-(x_1+ix_2)^2)}-x_2\}\,x_2 \gtrless 0 \qquad (17.10)$$

with

$$\nabla_2 \phi_m(x_1,0) = -\omega \qquad (17.11)$$

In fact it belongs to the flow around the slit with a velocity $\{0,\omega\}$, when observed by an observer who moves with the fluid at infinity so that the slit appears to move downward with the velocity $\{0,-\omega\}$. The jump in potential, or circulation, associated with this flow is evidently

$$\Gamma(x_1) = 2\omega \sqrt{(a^2 - x_1^2)} \tag{17.10'}$$

Since the graph of this function of x_1 is an ellipse, this distribution of circulation is also called "elliptic".

Incidentally, expression (15.14) for the velocity component u_2^∞ agrees with the formula

$$\int_{-a}^{+a} \frac{x_1'}{\sqrt{(a^2 - (x_1')^2)}} \frac{dx_1'}{x_1' - x_1} = \pi \tag{17.12}$$

which will be useful later on.

It is easily seen that, except for the factor ω, the flow potential $\phi_m(x)$ is uniquely determined by the condition (17.9) that the cross velocity be a given constant. For, the drag integral F_3 for the difference of two such potentials would be zero as seen after integration by parts. Accordingly, the flow with the potential (17.10) is the only one which minimizes the induced drag.

The value of the induced drag is easily calculated

$$F_3 = \tfrac{1}{2}\rho \iint |\nabla \phi_m|^2 \, dx_1 \, dx_2 = -\tfrac{1}{2}\rho \int_{-a}^{+a} \nabla_2 \phi_m \, \hat{\phi} \, dx_1$$

$$= \rho\omega^2 \int_{-a}^{+a} \sqrt{(a^2 - x_1^2)}$$

or
$$F_3 = \frac{\pi}{2}\rho\omega^2 a^2 \tag{17.13}$$

while the lift is

$$F_2 = 2\rho U_3^\infty \omega \int_{-a}^{+a} \sqrt{(a^2 - x_1^2)} \, dx_1$$

or
$$F_2 = \pi\rho U_3^\infty \omega a^2 \tag{17.14}$$

The ratio of induced drag to lift is

$$\frac{F_3}{F_2} = \frac{\omega}{2U_3^\infty}$$

Note that $\omega/2$ is the downwash velocity at the vortex line. Furthermore, as we shall see

$$F_3 = F_2^2 / [2\pi\rho \, a^2 (U_3^\infty)^2]$$

It is convenient to introduce the maximum circulation

$$\Gamma_0 = 2\omega a$$

by (17.10)' and to assume that it is connected with the chord b and the angle of attack α of the wing in the same way as for wings of infinite span

$$\Gamma_0 = \pi\alpha b U_3^\infty$$

We then find that

$$F_2 = \frac{\pi^2}{2}\rho(U_3^\infty)^2 \alpha S$$

where $S = ab$ in the surface area of one side of the wing.

Expressing α, Γ_0, and ω in terms of F_2 we find

$$\omega = F_2/[\pi\rho a^2 U_3^\infty]$$

and hence
$$F_3 = F_2^2/[2\pi\rho a^2(U_3^\infty)^2]$$

For a given value of the lift, therefore, the induced drag decreases with increasing speed. The opposite is, of course, true for the "skin friction" drag which results from the action of viscosity along the surfaces of the wing. It is more or less for this reason that airplanes designed to fly at high speed but not with great load are provided with relatively short wings.

CHAPTER 18

Determination of the Circulation

We now ask ourselves how we can determine the distribution of circulation around an airfoil of finite span from the shape and position of the airfoil.

The answer to this question given in the aerodynamic literature is the following:

Choose a plane $x_1 = x_1^0$ and then consider the two-dimensional flow past the airfoil of finite span with the profile of the actual airfoil at $x_1 = x_1^0$ as constant profile and with the velocity $\{0, u_2^{(3)}(x_1^0), U_3^\infty\}$ as velocity at infinity. According to the theory of two-dimensional flows the circulation $\Gamma(x_1^0)$ around the above airfoil of infinite span can be expressed from the shape of the airfoil in terms of U_3^∞ and $u_2^{(3)}(x_1^0)$ upon imposing the Kutta condition at the trailing edge. The resulting expression for $\Gamma(x_1)$ does not yet determine $\Gamma(x_1)$ since the value of $u_2^{(3)}(x_1^0)$ in its turn depends on the function $\Gamma(x_1)$. Nevertheless, this expression constitutes an integral equation for the function $\Gamma(x_1)$. The solution of this singular integral equation is then the desired circulation. The term $u_2^{(3)}(x_1^0)$ used above is the downwash velocity at the point $(x_1^0, 0, 0)$ of the flow with a vortex filament on $|x_1| \leqq a, x_2 = x_3 = 0$ which carries the circulation $\Gamma(x_1)$ to be determined, cf. (15.27).

We shall proceed to give a rigorous derivation of this procedure.

As before we describe the airfoil with the aid of two profile functions

$$x_2 = y^\pm(x_1, x_3) \tag{18.1}$$

while the base of the airfoil is described by the following inequalities

$$-\beta(x_1) \leqq x_3 \leqq \gamma(x_1), \qquad -a \leqq x_1 \leqq a \tag{18.2}$$

Furthermore, we set

$$y^+(x_1, -\beta(x_1)) = y^-(x_1, -\beta(x_1)) = y(x_1), \qquad -a \leqq x_1 \leqq a \tag{18.3}$$

and suppose that

$$y^+(x_1, \gamma(x_1)) = y^-(x_1, \gamma(x_1)) = 0, \qquad -a \leqq x_1 \leqq a \quad (18.4)$$

The quantity $\beta(x_1) + \gamma(x_1)$ is called the "chord" of the profile cut out by the plane $x_1 = $ constant while the ratio

$$\tan \alpha(x_1) = \frac{y(x_1)}{\beta(x_1) + \gamma(x_1)} \quad (18.5)$$

defines the "angle of attack" $\alpha(x_1)$ of the profile.

The potential function ϕ for the flow in excess of the parallel flow should satisfy the condition (cf. (14.5))

$$\nabla_2 \phi = U_3^\infty \nabla_3 y^\pm \quad (18.6)$$

on both sides of the base of the airfoil and on the base of the sheet, furthermore (cf. (14.9))

$$\hat{\phi}(x_1, 0, x_3) = \Gamma(x_1) \quad (18.7)$$

on the base of the sheet.

The function $\Gamma(x_1)$ is to be so determined that the Kutta condition is satisfied at the trailing edge $x_3 = \gamma(x_1), x_2 = 0, |x_1| \leqq a$ of the airfoil.

Instead of solving this problem exactly, we may, as we have done before, approximate the airfoil by a vortex filament. In doing this, however, it seems at first that we lose the possibility of determining the circulation by imposing the Kutta condition. Nevertheless, this circulation can be determined as we shall see by the following analysis.

We first consider a manifold $\mathcal{M}_b$ of similar airfoils whose maximum chord b shrinks to zero and we then determine the terms of lowest order in the expansion of the circulation with respect to the chord b. Suppose that the distribution of the chord is given by

$$x_3 = c(x_1, b) + d(x_1, b), \qquad -a \leqq x_1 \leqq a \quad (18.8)$$

over the span of the airfoil $\mathcal{M}_b$ where we have set

$$c(x_1, b) = b\gamma(x_1)$$

$$d(x_1, b) = b\beta(x_1)$$

Clearly $\gamma(x_1)$ and $\beta(x_1)$ are independent of b. For simplicity we suppose that

$$\max \{\gamma(x_1) + \beta(x_1)\} = 1$$

Suppose, furthermore, that the profile functions $\tilde{y}^{\pm}(x_1, x_3, b)$ of the members of $\mathcal{M}_b$ are in the form

$$\tilde{y}^{\pm}(x_1, x_3, b) = by^{\pm}\left(x_1, \frac{x_3}{b}\right) \tag{18.9}$$

where the functions $y^{\pm}(x_1, x_3)$ describe the profile of the airfoil we are considering and are, of course, independent of b. The base of the profile described by (18.9) can be seen to be described by the inequalities

$$-b\beta(x_1) \leqq x_3 \leqq b\gamma(x_1), \qquad -a \leqq x_1 \leqq a \tag{18.10}$$

using (18.1) and (18.2). Evidently

$$y(x_1) = \frac{1}{b}\tilde{y}(x_1, -b\beta(x_1), b) \tag{18.11}$$

where we have set

$$\tilde{y}(x_1, -b\beta(x_1), b) = \tilde{y}^{\pm}(x_1, -b\beta(x_1), b) \tag{18.12}$$

so that the angle of attack α defined by

$$\tan \alpha(x_1) = \frac{\tilde{y}(x_1, -b\beta(x_1), b)}{b[\beta(x_1)+\gamma(x_1)]} = \frac{y(x_1)}{\beta(x_1)+\gamma(x_1)} \tag{18.13}$$

is independent of b.

Our aim now is to determine the value of $\Gamma(x_1)$ for small values of b.

We assume that the potential function $\phi(x) = \phi(x, b)$ of the flow in excess to the parallel flow associated with the airfoil $\mathcal{M}_b$ possesses an expansion with respect to b of the form

$$\phi(x, b) = b\phi^{(1)}(x) + b^2 \phi^{(2)}(x) + ... \tag{18.14}$$

Accordingly, the circulation belonging to the flow with velocity potential $\phi(x, b)$ possesses an expansion

$$\Gamma(x_1, b) = b\Gamma^{(1)}(x_1) + b^2 \Gamma^{(2)}(x_1) + ... \tag{18.15}$$

Evidently when b tends to zero $\mathcal{M}_b$ shrinks to the line $x_2 = x_3 = 0$, $|x_1| \leqq a$. Consequently, $\phi^{(i)}(x)$ is defined outside of this line. In fact, the function $\phi^{(i)}(x)$ is exactly the potential function with circulation $\Gamma^{(i)}(x)$ distributed over the filaments $|x_1| \leqq a, x_2 = x_3 = 0$ treated in the previous chapters.

Our purpose is now to determine $\Gamma^{(i)}(x)$. To this end we perform a different expansion. We first stretch the airfoil while b shrinks to zero in such a way that its chord remains constant. More specifically we choose a point $x_1 = x_1^0$ on the trailing edge for which we want to determine the value of Γ. We then introduce new variables $\tilde{x}$ by

$$x_1 = x_1^0 + b\tilde{x}_1, \qquad x_2 = b\tilde{x}_2, \qquad x_3 = b\tilde{x}_3 \qquad (18.16)$$

so that the base of the airfoil becomes (cf. (18.10))

$$-\beta(x_1) \leqq \tilde{x}_3 \leqq \gamma(x_1)$$
$$-\frac{a+x_1^0}{b} \leqq \tilde{x}_1 \leqq \frac{a-x_1^0}{b} \qquad (18.17)$$

while the profile $\tilde{y}^{\pm}$ (cf. (18.9)) is described by

$$\tilde{x}_2 = y^{\pm}(x_1^0 + b\tilde{x}_1, \tilde{x}_3)$$

The angle of attack $\alpha(x_1)$ becomes

$$\alpha(x_1^0 + b\tilde{x}_1) \qquad (18.19)$$

Instead of the potential $\phi(x) = \phi(x, b)$ we introduce the potential $\tilde{\phi}(x, b)$

$$\tilde{\phi}(x, b) = \frac{1}{b}\phi(x, b) \qquad (18.20)$$

Denoting the circulation associated with the potential $\tilde{\phi}$ by $\tilde{\Gamma}(x, b)$ we have

$$\Gamma(x_1) = b\tilde{\Gamma}(x_1, b) \qquad (18.21)$$

The velocity remains unchanged; for

$$u(x) = \nabla\phi(x) = b^{-1}\tilde{\nabla}\phi(x) = \nabla\tilde{\phi}(x, b) = \tilde{u}(\tilde{x}) \qquad (18.22)$$

The condition on $\tilde{\phi}$ at the base of the airfoil and sheet thus becomes

$$\tilde{\nabla}_2 \tilde{\phi} = U_3^{\infty} \tilde{\nabla}_3 \tilde{y}^{\pm} \qquad (18.23)$$

while on the base of the sheet condition (18.7) becomes

$$\hat{\tilde{\phi}} = \tilde{\Gamma}(x_1, b) \qquad (18.24)$$

Clearly

$$\tilde{\phi}(x, b) = \phi^{(1)}(x) + b\phi^{(2)}(x) + \ldots \qquad (18.25)$$

We shall keep the first two terms in this expansion. For simplicity we denote them by $\tilde{\phi}$; thus

$$\tilde{\phi}(x, b) = \phi^{(1)}(x) + b\phi^{(2)}(x) \qquad (18.26)$$

Similarly we shall denote by $\tilde{\Gamma}$

$$\tilde{\Gamma}(x, b) = \Gamma^{(1)}(x) + b\Gamma^{(2)}(x)$$

In the limit as $b \to 0$, the base of the profile becomes

$$-\beta(x_1^0) \leq \tilde{x}_3 \leq \gamma(x_1^0), \qquad -\infty \leq \tilde{x}_1 \leq \infty \tag{18.27}$$

as can be seen from (18.16) and (18.17). Thus the base of the profile becomes an infinite strip of constant width. The description of the profile becomes

$$\tilde{x}_2 = \tilde{y}^\pm(x_1^0, \tilde{x}_3) \tag{18.28}$$

so that the profile becomes constant over the infinite span. The angle of attack also becomes a constant $\alpha(x_1^0)$ as we can see from (18.19). Conditions (18.23) and (18.24) on the potential $\tilde{\phi}(x)$ become

$$\tilde{\nabla}_2 \tilde{\phi} = U_3^\infty \tilde{\nabla}_3 \tilde{y}^\pm \tag{18.29}$$

on the base of the profile and sheet while

$$\overset{\circ}{\tilde{\phi}} = \tilde{\Gamma}^{(1)}(x_1^0, 0) \tag{18.30}$$

on the base of the sheet. The conditions which we impose on ϕ at infinity will be discussed below.

The function $\tilde{\Gamma}(x_1, b)$ can clearly be expressed using (18.15) as follows

$$\tilde{\Gamma}(x_1, b) = \Gamma^{(1)}(x_1) + b\Gamma^{(2)}(x_1) + \dots \tag{18.31}$$

whence for $b = 0$

$$\tilde{\Gamma}(x_1^0, 0) = \Gamma^{(1)}(x_1^0) \tag{18.32}$$

Thus we see that the circulation becomes a constant and that this constant is just the value of $\Gamma^{(1)}(x_1)$ for $x_1 = x_1^0$. As a consequence, the jump of potential is constant over the whole base of the sheet; in other words the vortex sheet has disappeared. However, as b tends to zero the manifold $\mathcal{M}_b$ tends to the vortex line $\mathcal{M}_0$. Accordingly we can approximate the potential for the flow around $\mathcal{M}_b$ by the potential associated with the vortex line $\mathcal{M}_0$ having circulation distribution $\Gamma(x_1, b)$. In accordance with (15.4) we have

$$\phi(x, b) = -\frac{1}{4\pi} \iint_{\mathscr{S}} \Gamma(x_1', b) \nabla_2 |x - x'|^{-1} ds$$

where $\mathscr{S}$ is the base of the vortex sheet.

The determination of the behavior to be imposed on $\tilde{\phi}(x, b)$ at infinity requires careful analysis. It would be futile to try to derive it from the behavior of $\phi(x)$ at infinity. For, as b approaches zero, any arbitrarily large portion of the $\tilde{x}$-space can be made to correspond to some small neighborhood of the point $x_1 = x_1^0, x_2 = 0, x_3 = 0$ in the x-space. Similarly, any finite region of the $\tilde{x}$-space corresponds to an arbitrarily small region around the point $x_1 = x_1^0, x_2 = 0, x_3 = 0$ in the x-space. The behavior of the function $\tilde{\phi}(\tilde{x})$ at infinity must, therefore, be related to the behavior of the function $\phi(x)$ at the point $x_1 = x_1^0, x_2 = x_3 = 0$. Accordingly, as $\tilde{x} \to \infty$ the velocity potential $\tilde{\phi}(x)$ should behave like $(1/b)\phi(x)$ in the neighborhood of the point $x_1 = x_1^0, x_2 = x_3 = 0$. From chapter 15, cf. (15.30), we have that near $x_2 = x_3 = 0$

$$\phi(x, b) \sim \frac{1}{2\pi} \Gamma(x_1, b) \arctan\left(-\frac{x_2}{x_1}\right) + x_2 u_2^{(3)}(x_1, 0, 0)$$

except possibly for an additive constant. Accordingly we have that near the point $(x_1^0, b\tilde{x}_2, b\tilde{x}_3)$

$$\tilde{\phi}(x, b) \sim \frac{\tilde{\Gamma}(x_1^0, b)}{2\pi} \arctan\left(-\frac{\tilde{x}_2}{\tilde{x}_3}\right) + \tilde{x}_2 u_2^{(3)}(x_1^0, 0) \qquad (18.33)$$

Thus at infinity the velocity should have the behavior

$$\tilde{u}(x) \sim u^{(1)}(x) + u_2^{(3)}(x) \qquad (18.34)$$

with
$$u^{(1)}(x) = \frac{\tilde{\Gamma}(x_1^0, b)}{2\pi} \left\{0, -\frac{\tilde{x}_3}{\tilde{x}_2^2 + \tilde{x}_3^2}, \frac{\tilde{x}_2}{\tilde{x}_2^2 + \tilde{x}_3^2}\right\} \qquad (18.35)$$

and
$$u_2^{(3)}(x_1^0, 0, 0) = \left\{0, \frac{b}{4\pi} \int_{-a}^{+a} \nabla_1' \tilde{\Gamma}(x_1', b) \frac{dx_1'}{x_1' - x_1^0}, 0\right\} \qquad (18.36)$$

where $\tilde{\Gamma}$ is given by (18.31). Note that conditions on $\tilde{u}$ now formulated are consistent with purely two-dimensional flow around the airfoil of infinite span with constant profile given by (18.27) and (18.28). The velocity field given by (18.34), (18.35), (18.36) behaves at infinity like a purely two-dimensional irrotational flow with counter circulation $\tilde{\Gamma}(x_1^0, b)$ combined with a parallel downwash flow. Accordingly the behavior of the total velocity at infinity is given by

$$U + \tilde{u} \sim \{0, u_2^{(3)}(x_1^0), U_3^\infty\} + \frac{1}{2\pi} \tilde{\Gamma}(x_1^0, b) \left\{0, -\frac{\tilde{x}_3}{\tilde{x}_2^2 + \tilde{x}_3^2}, \frac{\tilde{x}_2}{\tilde{x}_2^2 + \tilde{x}_3^2}\right\} \qquad (18.37)$$

where $u_2^{(3)}(x_1^0)$ is the downwash velocity

$$u_2^{(3)}(x_1^0) = \frac{b}{4\pi} \int_{-a}^{+a} \nabla_1' \tilde{\Gamma}(x_1', b) \frac{dx_1'}{x_1' - x_1^0} \qquad (18.38)$$

The flow with this behavior at infinity is nothing but the two-dimensional flow past the airfoil of infinite span with a constant profile, namely, the profile at $x_1 = x_1^0$, having at infinity a velocity consisting of the original velocity combined with the downwash velocity at the profile plus a velocity corresponding to a circulation $\tilde{\Gamma}(x_1^0, b)$. The circulation of this flow determined with the aid of the Kutta-Joukowski theory is therefore the derived circulation. Thus we have arrived at the prescription given above for determining the circulation (i.e. for $b = 1$).

From the Joukowski theory of two-dimensional flows around simple wing profiles we have that

$$\Gamma(x_1) = 4\pi a(x_1) U^\infty(x_1) \sin(\alpha(x_1) + \beta(x_1)) \qquad (18.39)$$

where $\alpha(x_1)$ and $\beta(x_1)$ depend upon the conformal mapping of the exterior of the profile onto a region exterior to a circular region ($a(x_1)$ is the radius of this region) and $\alpha(x_1)$ is the angle of attack of the profile. $U^\infty(x_1)$ is the absolute value of the velocity at infinity. Accordingly

$$\tilde{\Gamma}(x_1^0, b) = 4\pi a(x_1^0) \sin \beta(x_1^0) U_3^\infty - 4\pi a(x_1^0) \cos \beta(x_1^0) u_2^{(3)}(x_1^0) \qquad (18.40)$$

so that keeping terms of order less than or equal to b we obtain

$$\Gamma^{(1)}(x_1^0) + b\Gamma^{(2)}(x_1^0) = 4\pi a(x_1^0) \sin \beta(x_1^0) U_3^\infty$$
$$-4\pi a(x_1^0) \cos \beta(x_1^0) \frac{b}{\pi} \int_{-a}^{+a} \frac{\nabla_1' \Gamma^{(1)}(x_1')}{(x_1' - x_1^0)} dx_1' \qquad (18.41)$$

Equating coefficients of equal powers of b on both sides of the last relation we obtain

$$\Gamma^{(1)}(x_1^0) = 4\pi a(x_1^0) \sin \beta(x_1^0) U_3^\infty$$
$$\Gamma^{(2)}(x_1^0) = -a(x_1^0) \cos \beta(x_1^0) \int_{-a}^{+a} \frac{\nabla_1' \Gamma^{(1)}(x_1^0)}{(x_1' - x_1^0)} dx_1' \qquad (18.42)$$

The relationship between profile and velocity at infinity for two dimensional flow is very simple when the angle of attack is so small that the first order approximation to the flow may be employed. It is given by the formula

$$\Gamma = \mu \, d\alpha U^\infty \qquad (18.43)$$

5

where μ is a numerical factor depending on the shape of the profile, in the first approximation $\mu = \pi$. Furthermore, d is the depth and α is the angle of attack, i.e. the angle between the chord of the profile and the velocity at infinity. The angle of attack $\alpha(x_1)$ which was introduced above refers to the velocity $\{0, 0, U_3^\infty\}$ at infinity. According to the prescription we have derived we should take the velocity $\{0, u_2^{(3)}(x_1), U_3^\infty\}$ at infinity. Since $u_2^{(3)}(x_1)$ is small compared with U_3^∞, the "effective" angle of attack may simply be given as

$$\alpha_{\text{eff}}(x_1) = \alpha(x_1) + \frac{u_2^{(3)}(x_1)}{U_3^\infty}$$

Note that $u_2^{(3)}(x_1)$ is negative and hence $\alpha_{\text{eff}} < \alpha$.

Inserting the expression (18.38) for $u_2^{(3)}(x)$ and replacing b by $c(x_1) + b(x_1) = b[\beta(x_1) + \gamma(x_1)]$ in formula (18.43), this formula becomes

$$[\mu b[\beta(x_1) + \gamma(x_1)]^{-1} \Gamma(x_1)$$

$$-\frac{1}{4\pi} \int_{-a}^{+a} \nabla_1' \Gamma(x_1') \frac{dx_1'}{x_1' - x_1} = \alpha(x_1) U_3^\infty \qquad (18.44)$$

This equation is an *integral equation for the approximate determination of the circulation* $\Gamma(x_1)$. Calculation of the circulation distribution using equations (18.41), however, probably gives more accurate results.

Relation (18.43) enables us to set up conditions on depth and angle of attack for an airfoil that leads to the minimum induced drag with a given lift. From the results of chapter 17 we know that the circulation for such an airfoil is given by

$$\Gamma(x_1) = 2\omega \sqrt{(a^2 - x_1^2)}$$

where $-\omega/2$ is the downwash velocity at the vortex filament, or

$$\omega = -\frac{1}{2\pi} \int_{-a}^{+a} \nabla_1' \Gamma(x_1') \frac{dx_1'}{x_1' - x_1}$$

Relation (18.43) therefore leads to the condition that

$$[\mu(b(x_1) + c(x_1))]^{-1} \sqrt{(a^2 - x_1^2)} - \tfrac{1}{2} = \frac{\alpha(x_1)}{\omega} U_3^\infty$$

from which we conclude that

$$2[\mu(b(x_1) + c(x_1))\alpha(x_1)]^{-1} \sqrt{(a^2 - x_1^2)} - [\alpha(x_1)]^{-1}$$

must be a constant. This condition can be satisfied by taking α as a constant and setting

$$c(x_1) + b(x_1) = b_0 \, a^{-1} \sqrt{(a^2 - x_1^2)}$$

with

$$ab_0^{-1} = \mu \left[\tfrac{1}{2} + \frac{\alpha}{\omega} U_3^\infty \right]$$

Accordingly, the airfoil having minimum induced drag for a given lift would have the shape of an ellipse.

CHAPTER 19

Motion of Single Vortex Filaments

The basic laws of motion of straight vortex filaments in two-dimensional flow were derived earlier, in chapter 3. In the present chapter we shall discuss more generally the motion of such vortices while in chapter 20 we shall discuss the theory of vortex streets.

Suppose that n vortex filaments are present in a fluid which fills the whole space and which is furthermore at rest at infinity. We suppose further that the flow in question is two-dimensional. Accordingly, it is sufficient to consider the flow in the (x, y)-plane or equivalently in the z-plane where we set

$$z = x + iy$$

Let the n vortices $\mathscr{V}_k, k = 1, \ldots, n$, be located at the n points $z_k, k = 1, \ldots, n$ respectively, and denote the circulation of the vortex $\mathscr{V}_k$ by $\Gamma_k = 2\pi\gamma_k$. We know that the flow is completely determined by the location and circulation of these vortices. In fact, according to the theory developed in chapter 3, the complex potential

$$\chi = \phi + i\psi \tag{19.1}$$

is given by (cf. (3.2).)

$$\chi(z, t) = -i \sum_{m=1}^{n} \gamma_m \log(z - z_m(t)) + \mathscr{R}(z)$$

up to an aribitrary additive constant. The velocity $w = u + iv = d\bar{\chi}/d\bar{z}$ is then

$$w(z, t) = i \sum_{m=1}^{n} \frac{\gamma_m}{\bar{z} - \bar{z}_m(t)} + \overline{\mathscr{R}'(z)}$$

The condition that the fluid be at rest at infinity implies that $w(z, t)$ and hence also $\mathscr{R}'(z)$ vanishes at infinity. Since the latter function is regular

121

in the whole plane it is identically zero by Liouville's theorem. Consequently, we have

$$\chi(z, t) = i \sum_{m=1}^{n} \gamma_m \log(z - z_m(t)) \tag{19.2}$$

$$w(z, t) = i \sum_{m=1}^{n} \frac{\gamma_m}{\bar{z} - \bar{z}_m(t)} \tag{19.3}$$

According to (3.12), the velocity $dz_k(t)/dt$ of the vortex $\mathscr{V}_k$ is the regular part of this velocity w, so that

$$\frac{dz_k(t)}{dt} = i \sum_{m \neq k} \frac{\gamma_m}{\bar{z}_k(t) - \bar{z}_m(t)}, \qquad k = 1, ..., n \tag{19.4}$$

The motion of the system of vortices is therefore governed by this system of n-differential equations of first order.

It is a remarkable fact that these equations of motion possess three integrals:

$$M = \sum_{m=1}^{n} \gamma_m z_m(t) \tag{19.5}$$

$$I = \sum_{m=1}^{n} \gamma_m |z_m(t)|^2 \tag{19.6}$$

$$H = \sum_{k > m} \gamma_k \gamma_m \log |z_k(t) - z_m(t)|; \tag{19.7}$$

in the latter sum the pair of subscripts (k, m) are to run over all pairs of values from $k = 1, ..., n, m = 1, ..., n$, each pair taken once and the pairs with $k = m$ being excluded.

The fact that (19.5), (19.6) and (19.7) are constants of the motion can be immediately verified. From (19.4) we can easily derive the relation

$$\sum \gamma_k \frac{dz_k(t)}{dt} = 0 \tag{19.5}'$$

for, in the sum on the right hand side of (19.4) with every member its negative occurs. Equation (19.6) can be derived as follows: note that

$$\sum_k \sum_{m \neq k} \frac{\gamma_m \gamma_k \bar{z}_k}{\bar{z}_k(t) - \bar{z}_m(t)} = \sum_{m > k} \gamma_m \gamma_k$$

so that

$$\sum \gamma_k \bar{z}_k(t) \frac{dz_k(t)}{dt} = i \sum_{m > k} \gamma_m \gamma_k$$

or
$$\text{Re} \sum \gamma_k \bar{z}_k(t) \frac{dz_k(t)}{dt} = 0 \tag{19.6)'}$$

which implies
$$\sum \gamma_k \frac{d|z_k(t)|^2}{dt} = 0$$

To derive (19.7) note that using (19.4)

$$\sum_k \gamma_k \frac{dz_k}{dt}\frac{d\bar{z}_k}{dt} = \sum_k i \sum_{m>k} \frac{\gamma_m \gamma_k (z_k(t) - z_m(t)) d\bar{z}_k}{|z_k(t) - z_m(t)|^2} \frac{d\bar{z}_k}{dt}$$

or

$$\sum_k \gamma_k \frac{dz_k}{dt}\frac{d\bar{z}_k}{dt} = i \sum_{k>m} \frac{\gamma_m \gamma_k (z_k(t) - z_m(t)) \frac{d}{dt}(\bar{z}_k - \bar{z}_m)}{|z_k(t) - z_m(t)|^2} \tag{19.7)'}$$

Since the left hand side of (19.7)' is clearly real the real part of the sum on the right hand side must vanish and this real part is nothing but the derivative of (19.7).

If the numbers γ_k could be interpreted as masses the integral M would correspond to the moment of masses while I would be the moment of inertia and H, the "Kirchhoff function", could be interpreted as an energy. We note, however, that the numbers γ_k need not be positive.

The fact that the three quantities M, I, and H are constants of the motion could, of course, also be verified directly by differentiation. However, we can proceed differently. We consider for this purpose the function H as a function of $z_1, ..., z_n, \bar{z}_1, ..., \bar{z}_n$ and verify immediately the relation

$$\frac{\partial H}{\partial \bar{z}_k} = \frac{\gamma_k}{2} \sum_{m \neq k} \frac{\gamma_m}{\bar{z}_k - \bar{z}_m} \tag{19.8}$$

Expression (19.4) for the velocity dz_k/dt can thus be written in the form

$$\gamma_k \frac{dz_k}{dt} = 2i \frac{\partial H}{\partial \bar{z}_k} \tag{19.9}$$

Taking the complex conjugate of the last expression we obtain

$$\gamma_k \frac{d\bar{z}_k}{dt} = -2i \frac{\partial H}{\partial z_k} \tag{19.10}$$

Instead of taking $z_k, \bar{z}_k, k = 1, ..., n$ we may take $x_k = \frac{1}{2}(z_k + \bar{z}_k)$ and $y_k = (1/2i)(z_k - \bar{z}_k)$ as independent variables. We then have

$$\frac{\partial}{\partial x_k} = \frac{\partial}{\partial z_k} + \frac{\partial}{\partial \bar{z}_k} \tag{19.11}$$

and

$$\frac{\partial}{\partial y_k} = i\left(\frac{\partial}{\partial z_k} - \frac{\partial}{\partial \bar{z}_k}\right) \tag{19.12}$$

Using the last two relations together with (19.10) and (19.9) we obtain

$$\gamma_k \frac{dx_k}{dt} = -\frac{\partial H}{\partial y_k} \tag{19.13}$$

and

$$\gamma_k \frac{dy_k}{dt} = \frac{\partial H}{\partial x_k} \tag{19.14}$$

The system of differential equations (19.13), (19.14) is similar in structure to the Hamilton-Jacobi equations in Dynamics. The statement that the quantities M, I, H are constants of the motion can be derived in the same way as the analogous statements in that theory.

Accordingly, after setting $z_k = z_k(t)$ and $\bar{z}_k = \bar{z}_k(t)$ and using (19.13) and (19.14), we find

$$\frac{dH}{dt} = \sum_k \frac{\partial H}{\partial y_k} \frac{dy_k}{dt} + \frac{\partial H}{\partial x_k} \frac{dx_k}{dt} \tag{19.15}$$

$$= -\sum_k \gamma_k \left(\frac{dx_k}{dt} \frac{dy_k}{dt} - \frac{dy_k}{dt} \frac{dx_k}{dt}\right) = 0$$

whence $H = \text{const.}$

We next observe, in view of the definition of H in (19.7), that the relation

$$H(z_1, ..., z_n) = H(z_1 + \zeta, ..., z_n + \zeta) \tag{19.16}$$

holds when $\zeta = \xi + i\eta$ is an arbitrary constant. Differentiating relation (19.16) with respect to ξ and η and setting $\zeta = 0$ we find

$$\sum_k \frac{\partial H}{\partial x_k} = 0 \tag{19.17}$$

and

$$\sum_k \frac{\partial H}{\partial y_k} = 0 \tag{19.18}$$

whence by (19.13) and (19.14)

$$\frac{d}{dt}\sum_k \gamma_k y_k = 0, \qquad \frac{d}{dt}\sum_k \gamma_k x_k = 0 \qquad (19.19)$$

so that $M = $ const. follows.

We next observe that the relation

$$H(z_1, ..., \bar{z}_n) = H(z_1 e^{i\theta}, ..., \bar{z}_n e^{-i\theta}) \qquad (19.20)$$

holds for arbitrary real θ, as can be easily seen from (19.6). Differentiating (19.20) with respect to θ and setting $\theta = 0$ we find

$$\sum_k \left(z_k \frac{\partial H}{\partial z_k} - \bar{z}_k \frac{\partial H}{\partial \bar{z}_k} \right) = 0 \qquad (19.21)$$

whence, using (19.9) and (19.10), we have

$$\sum_k \gamma_k z_k \frac{\partial \bar{z}_k}{\partial t} + \gamma_k \bar{z}_k \frac{\partial z_k}{\partial t} = 0 \qquad (19.22)$$

which implies that $I = $ const.

The discussion of the motion of a set of vortices is naturally greatly simplified by the existence of these three constants of motion. We proceed to discuss a few typical examples.

We consider first *one pair of vortices* $\mathcal{V}_1, \mathcal{V}_2$. We distinguish two cases: Case I where $\gamma_1 + \gamma_2 \neq 0$ and Case II where $\gamma_1 + \gamma_2 = 0$. In case $\gamma_1 + \gamma_2 \neq 0$ we can choose the origin of the coordinate system such that

$$M = \gamma_1 z_1 + \gamma_2 z_2 = 0$$

as one easily verifies. We then set

$$\gamma_1 z_1 = -\gamma_2 z_2 = \zeta e^{i\theta} \qquad (19.23)$$

with ζ real and positive. From the relation $I = $ const. we obtain

$$\left(\frac{1}{\gamma_1} + \frac{1}{\gamma_2} \right) |\zeta|^2 = \text{const.} \qquad (19.24)$$

which implies that ζ is a constant since $\gamma_1 + \gamma_2 \neq 0$. In this case, the relation $H = $ const. implies that $|z_1 - z_2| = $ const. which is already a consequence of the other deductions; for,

$$z_1 - z_2 = \zeta e^{i\theta} \left[\frac{1}{\gamma_1} + \frac{1}{\gamma_2} \right] \qquad (19.25)$$

We therefore may conclude that the two vortices move on two circles with center at the origin and whose radii R_1, R_2 are inversely proportional to their circulations, as we can see from (19.23). Relation (19.23), furthermore, tells us that at each time the two vortices lie on the same radius, which rotates with angular velocity

$$\frac{d\theta}{dt} = \frac{1}{i}\frac{\gamma_1}{\zeta e^{i\theta}}\frac{dz_1}{dt} = \frac{\gamma_1\gamma_2}{\zeta e^{i\theta}}\frac{1}{\bar{z}_1 - \bar{z}_2}$$

or
$$\frac{d\theta}{dt} = \frac{\gamma_1^2\gamma_2^2}{\gamma_1 + \gamma_2}\cdot\frac{1}{\zeta^2} \tag{19.26}$$

This is seen upon making use of (19.23) and (19.4), see Fig 19.1.

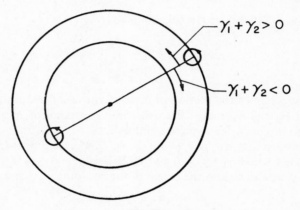

Fig. 19.1.

In Case II, $\gamma_1 + \gamma_2 = 0$ the relation $M = \text{const.}$ gives

$$z_1 - z_2 = \text{const.} \tag{19.27}$$

By a rotation of the coordinate system we can always make

$$x_2 - x_1 = 0 \tag{19.28}$$

We set $y_2 - y_1 = \delta$. Relation $I = \text{const.}$ then reduces to

$$|z_1|^2 - |z_2|^2 = \text{const.} \tag{19.29}$$

from which we conclude that

$$\text{Im}(z_1 + z_2) = \text{const.} \tag{19.30}$$

For, as we can easily check

$$|z_1|^2 - |z_2|^2 = y_1^2 - y_2^2 = (y_1 - y_2)(y_1 + y_2) = -\delta \operatorname{Im}(z_1 + z_2)$$

The constant $y_1 + y_2$ can be made zero by a shift of the coordinate system

$$y_1 + y_2 = 0 \tag{19.31}$$

The equation of motion finally reduces to

$$\frac{dx_1}{dt} = \frac{dx_2}{dt} = -\frac{\gamma_1}{\delta} = \frac{\gamma_2}{\delta} \tag{19.32}$$

It follows that the pair of vortices moves with a constant velocity as indicated in Fig. 19.2.

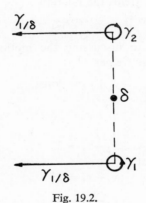

Fig. 19.2.

Case $\gamma_1 + \gamma_2 = 0$

We next consider the motion of *two vortices* $\mathcal{V}_1, \mathcal{V}_2$ with circulations γ_1, γ_2 respectively, and in the presence of a wall. We suppose that the wall is given by the line $x_2 = 0$ and that the vortices lie in the half plane $x_2 > 0$.

The solution of the flow problem, the complex velocity potential $\chi(x) = \phi + i\psi$, is determined up to a constant. Furthermore, the line $x_2 = 0$ should be a streamline, i.e. $\psi = $ const.; in particular, we choose the additive constant so that $\psi = 0$ on the line $x_2 = 0$. We can now reflect the resulting flow about the line $x_2 = 0$ using the well-known principle of reflection so that

$$\chi(\bar{z}) = \overline{\chi(z)} \tag{19.33}$$

By this reflection we obtain a flow in the finite plane consisting of four vortices $z_1, z_2, \bar{z}_1, \bar{z}_2$ having respectively the circulations $\gamma_1, \gamma_2, -\gamma_1, -\gamma_2$. From the relation $M = $ const. we obtain

$$\gamma_1 y_1 + \gamma_2 y_2 = \text{const.} \tag{19.34}$$

The relation $I = 0$ is satisfied identically. Since

$$H = \sum_{m>k} \gamma_m \gamma_k \log |z_m - z_k|$$

$$= \log |2y_1|^{-\gamma_1^2} |2y_2|^{-\gamma_2^2} |z_1 - z_2|^{2\gamma_1\gamma_2} |z_1 - \bar{z}_2|^{-2\gamma_1\gamma_2}$$

the relation $H = $ const. yields the relation

$$|y_1|^{-\gamma_1^2} |y_2|^{-\gamma_2^2} |z_1 - z_2|^{2\gamma_1\gamma_2} |z_1 - \bar{z}_2|^{-2\gamma_1\gamma_2} = \text{const.} \tag{19.35}$$

We confine ourselves to discussing the motion in the case where $\gamma_1 = \gamma_2 = \gamma$. In this case we get

$$y_1 + y_2 = \text{const.} \tag{19.36}$$

by (19.34). We set

$$y_1 + y_2 = 2\delta \tag{19.37}$$

and further we set

$$z_2 - z_1 = 2\zeta \tag{19.38}$$

where $\zeta = \xi + i\eta$, so that

$$x_2 - x_1 = 2\xi \tag{19.39}$$

$$y_2 - y_1 = 2\eta \tag{19.40}$$

The variable ζ describes the relative motion of the point $\mathscr{V}_2$ with respect to $\mathscr{V}_1$. We shall now find various possibilities for this relative motion.

Evidently,

$$\delta^2 - \eta^2 = y_1 y_2 > 0 \tag{19.41}$$

and

$$z_1 - \bar{z}_2 = -2\xi + 2\delta i \tag{19.42}$$

Upon substituting (19.39), (19.40) and (19.37) in (19.35) we therefore get

$$(\delta^2 - \eta^2)^{-\gamma^2} (\xi^2 + \eta^2)^{\gamma^2} (\xi^2 + \delta^2)^{-\gamma^2} = \text{const.} \tag{19.43}$$

or, $$(\delta^2-\eta^2)(\xi^2+\delta^2)(\xi^2+\eta^2)^{-1} = \text{const.} \qquad (19.44)$$

Denoting this constant by σ^2 we have

$$(\delta^2-\eta^2)(\xi^2+\delta^2) = \sigma^2(\xi^2+\eta^2) \qquad (19.45)$$

The last relation involves only the variables ξ and η. Solving it for η^2 we get

$$\eta^2 = \frac{\delta^4+(\delta^2-\sigma^2)\xi^2}{\xi^2+\delta^2+\sigma^2} \qquad (19.46)$$

The curve given by this equation passes through the points $\xi = 0$, $\eta = \pm\eta_0$ with

$$\eta_0 = \frac{\delta^2}{\sqrt{(\delta^2+\sigma^2)}} \qquad (19.47)$$

Note that

$$\eta_0 < \delta$$

We must distinguish between the two cases, $\sigma > \delta$ and $\sigma \leqq \delta$. We consider first the case $\sigma \leqq \delta$. The right member of (19.46) then gives the positions for all ξ. Clearly, as $\xi^2 \to \infty$, $\eta^2 \to \delta^2-\sigma^2$ so that in this case the curve $\eta(\xi)$ runs as in Fig. 19.3.

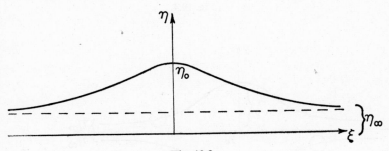

Fig. 19.3.

Clearly

$$\eta_0 > \eta_\infty = \sqrt{(\delta^2-\sigma^2)}$$

We note that in this case

$$\eta_0 > \frac{\delta}{\sqrt{2}} \qquad (19.48)$$

as may be seen from (19.47).

Secondly, we consider the case $\sigma > \delta$. In this case the right member of (19.46) becomes negative for $|\xi| > \xi_0 = \delta/\sqrt{(\sigma^2 - \delta^2)}$ and accordingly the curve is closed and may look as in Fig. 19.4.

We have so far described the relative motion of two vortices in the presence of a wall. From (19.36) we see that the mean of the y ordinates of the two vortices must be fixed. From Fig. 19.3 in the case $\sigma < \delta$ we

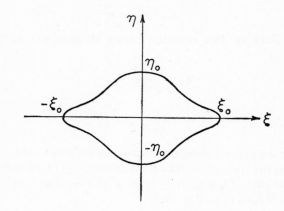

Fig. 19.4.

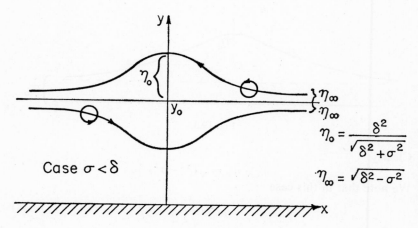

$$\eta_0 = \frac{\delta^2}{\sqrt{\delta^2 + \sigma^2}}$$

$$\eta_\infty = \sqrt{\delta^2 - \sigma^2}$$

Case $\sigma < \delta$

Fig. 19.5.

see that the two vortices move along a path as described in Fig. 19.5. In the case $\sigma \geqq \delta$ we see that the path looks as in Fig. 19.6.

$$\xi_0 = \frac{\delta}{\sqrt{(\sigma^2 - \delta^2)}} \qquad \eta_0 = \frac{\delta^2}{\sqrt{(\delta^2 + \sigma^2)}} \qquad \delta = y_0$$

In this case we have

$$\frac{y_2^0}{y_1^0} = \frac{\delta + \dfrac{\delta^2}{\sqrt{(\delta^2 + \sigma^2)}}}{\delta - \dfrac{\delta^2}{\sqrt{(\delta^2 + \sigma^2)}}} = \frac{[\sqrt{(\delta^2 + \sigma^2)} + \delta^2]^2}{\sigma^2} \leqq [\sqrt{(2)} + 1]^2$$

since $\delta \leqq \sigma$. Thus if $y_2^0/y_1^0 \geqq 5.828$ the two vortices move independently, whereas, if $y_2^0/y_1^0 \leqq 5.828$ they move as in Fig. 19.6.

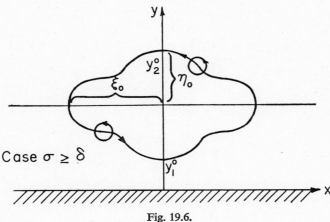

Fig. 19.6.

CHAPTER 20

Vortex Streets

In this chapter we shall consider the motion of a sequence of vortices $\mathscr{V}_i$ in some very special configurations known as vortex streets. As in the previous chapter we shall suppose that the vortices lie in a plane and represent the motion of straight vortex filaments present in a fluid which fills the whole space, so that we can consider the flow in the z-plane with $z = x_1 + ix_2$.

We consider first the motion of a single vortex street formed by an infinite sequence of vortices situated in equally spaced positions along a straight line. Without loss in generality we suppose that the vortices $\mathscr{V}_k$ are situated along the x_1 axis at the points $z_k = 2kd$ $(k = 0, \pm 1, \pm 2, ...)$ with d real.

We suppose further that these vortices have constant circulation

$$C = -\Gamma = -2\pi\gamma \tag{20.1}$$

From the previous chapter we see that in a purely formal way the complex velocity potential of this flow can be written as

$$\chi(z) = \gamma \sum_k{}' \log\left(1 - \frac{z}{2kd}\right) + i\gamma \log z \tag{20.2}$$

since $\chi(z)$ is determined up to an additive constant for each vortex. In this case it can be shown that

$$\chi(z) = i\gamma \log z \, \Pi'\left(1 - \frac{z}{2kd}\right) \tag{20.3}$$

Using the well-known infinite product representation of the sine

$$\sin z = z \, \Pi'_n\left(1 - \frac{z}{n\pi}\right) \tag{20.4}$$

we therefore have

$$\chi(z) = i\gamma \log \sin\left(\frac{\pi}{2d}z\right) \tag{20.5}$$

The derivative of this function is

$$\overline{w(z)} = \frac{d\chi(z)}{dz} = \frac{i\gamma\pi}{2d} \cot\frac{\pi}{2d}z \tag{20.6}$$

Indicating the regular part of a function with respect to z for $z = 0$ by Reg, we then have

$$\overline{w}_R(0) = \frac{i\gamma\pi}{2d} \operatorname{Reg} \frac{\cos\dfrac{\pi z}{2d}}{\sin\dfrac{\pi z}{2d}}$$

$$= \frac{i\gamma\pi}{2d} \operatorname{Reg} \frac{1}{\dfrac{\pi z}{2d} - \dfrac{1}{3!}\left(\dfrac{\pi z}{2d}\right)^3 + \cdots}$$

$$= \frac{i\gamma\pi}{2d} \operatorname{Reg} \frac{1}{\dfrac{\pi z}{2d}} \cdot \left(1 + \frac{1}{3!}\left(\frac{\pi z}{2d}\right)^2 + \cdots\right)$$

or
$$\overline{w}_R(0) = 0 \tag{20.7}$$

Similarly

$$\overline{w}_R(z_k) = 0$$

Incidentally this fact is an immediate consequence of the k symmetry. Furthermore, as $y \to \pm\infty$ we have upon using (20.6) that

$$\lim_{y \to \pm\infty} \overline{w(z)} \to \pm\frac{\gamma\pi}{2d} \tag{20.8}$$

so that the velocity at infinity does not vanish although the vortex points remain at rest.

We consider next a double vortex street formed by two parallel single vortex streets having the same distance $2d$ and with opposite circulations. We suppose further that two single vortex streets lie on the lines

$x_2 = \pm\eta$ so that their distance is 2η. Specifically, we suppose that the vortices η_k are situated at the points

$$z_k = \zeta + 2kd, \qquad \zeta = \xi + i\eta, \qquad c = -2\pi\gamma \qquad (20.9)$$

$$z'_k = -\zeta + 2kd, \qquad c = +2\pi\gamma, \qquad k = 0, \pm 1, \pm 2, \ldots \quad (20.10)$$

From the above considerations we see that the complex velocity potential becomes

$$\chi(z) = i\gamma \log \frac{\sin\dfrac{\pi(z-\zeta)}{2d}}{\sin\dfrac{\pi(z+\zeta)}{2d}} \qquad (20.11)$$

Consequently,

$$\bar{w}(z) = \frac{i\gamma\pi}{2d}\left[\cot\frac{\pi(z-\zeta)}{2d} - \cot\frac{\pi(z+\zeta)}{2d}\right] \qquad (20.12)$$

or

$$\bar{w}(z) = \frac{i\gamma\pi}{2d}\left[\frac{\sin\dfrac{\pi\zeta}{d}}{\sin\dfrac{\pi(z-\zeta)}{2d}\sin\dfrac{\pi(z+\zeta)}{2d}}\right]$$

whence

$$\bar{w}(z) = \frac{i\gamma\pi}{d}\frac{\sin\dfrac{\pi\zeta}{d}}{\cos\dfrac{\pi\zeta}{d} - \cos\dfrac{\pi z}{d}} \qquad (20.13)$$

From equation (20.13) we find $\bar{w}(z) \to 0$ as $|y| \to \infty$; in fact $\bar{w}(z)$ vanishes exponentially. Furthermore, from (20.12) we have

$$\bar{w}_R(\zeta) = -\frac{i\gamma\pi}{2d}\cot\frac{\pi\zeta}{d} \qquad (20.14)$$

or

$$w_R(\zeta) = +\frac{i\gamma\pi}{2d}\cot\frac{\pi\bar{\zeta}}{d}$$

We now consider two cases: The first case, the case of a symmetric street, occurs when $\xi = 0$, $\zeta = i\eta$, see Fig. 20.1. According to (20.14) we have

$$w_R(\zeta) = -\frac{\gamma\pi}{2d}\coth\frac{\pi\eta}{d} \qquad (20.15)$$

The second case, see Fig. 20.2, the case of an antisymmetric street, occurs when

$$\zeta = \frac{d}{2} + i\eta$$

From (20.14) we then have

$$w_R(\zeta) = \frac{i\gamma\pi}{2d}\tan-\frac{i\pi\eta}{d} = \frac{\pi\gamma}{2d}\tanh\frac{\pi\eta}{d} \tag{20.16}$$

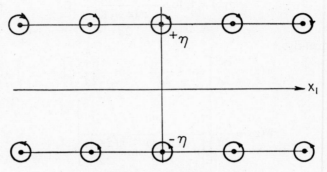

Fig. 20.1.   Symmetric vortex street.

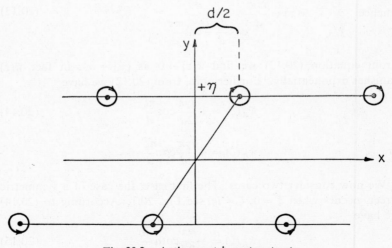

Fig. 20.2.   Antisymmetric vortex street.

In this case we notice that the vortex points on one side of the street lie opposite to the midpoints of the segments of length $2d$ on the other side of the street.

The latter case is the one which occurs in nature and has been shown by von Karman to be the only stable case.

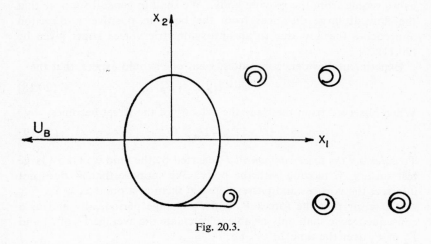

Fig. 20.3.

The importance of the theory of vortex streets lies in the use that von Karman made of them in expressing *the forces on a rigid body in a flow* in terms of the dimensions and velocity of the street independent of the shape of the body. (Of course, dimensions and velocity of the street themselves do depend on the shape of the body.) We now proceed to discuss the method of calculating the forces on a rigid body in uniform motion in a fluid.

Consider a body symmetric about the x_1-axis and moving through a fluid of density ρ in the negative x_1-direction with constant velocity U_B ($U_B < 0$ in the figure). In the flows which are actually observed in nature an antisymmetric half vortex street leaves the body as in Fig. 20.3. Accordingly we suppose that an anti-symmetric half vortex street leaves the body and then we shall calculate the average force exerted by the fluid on the body. We suppose that the velocity of the fluid at infinity is zero and that the vortices of the shed half vortex street attain a constant velocity $W_R = U_R$ at large distances from the body.

This velocity should tend to the velocity of the full double vortex street with the same dimensions

$$U_R = \frac{\pi\gamma}{2d}\tanh\frac{\pi\eta}{d} \tag{20.17}$$

as we recede from the moving body. We shall in general suppose that the flow at large distances from the body in positive x_1-direction approaches the flow due to an anti-symmetric vortex street given by (20.11).

Experimental evidence indicates, what one should expect, that the

$$0 < -U_R < -U_B \tag{20.18}$$

When observed from the body the velocity of the street becomes

$$U^T = U_R - U_B > 0 \tag{20.19}$$

To *calculate the force component* F_1 exerted by the fluid we take a large test surface $\mathscr{T}$ moving with the body. We suppose that $\mathscr{T}$ does not intersect the vortices and passes between them at a point $x_1 = x_0$.

It is clear that the forces F_1 and F_2 change periodically and as a consequence we shall only be able to calculate the average $\tilde{F}_1$ of F_1 and $\tilde{F}_2$ of F_2 over the time $2d/U^T$, i.e.

$$\tilde{F}_1(t) = \frac{U^T}{2d}\int_t^{t+U^T/2d} F_1(t')\,dt'; \tag{20.20}$$

however, we also see that $\tilde{F}_2 = 0$, owing to symmetry. Furthermore the average rate of change of momentum contained in the interior of $\mathscr{T}$ vanishes since the configuration is repeated after formation of two new vortices, i.e. after the time $2d/U^T$.

When observed from the body the velocity of flow is $u - U_B = u + U^\infty$, where we define $U^\infty = -U_B$. We now define $'F_1$ as the resultant of the pressure forces in x_1-direction on the test surface plus momentum influx through $\mathscr{T}$. Thus, setting

$$'F_1 = -\oint_{\mathscr{T}} p\,dy - \oint_{\mathscr{T}} \rho(u_1+U^\infty)\{(u_1+U^\infty)\,dy - u_2\,dx\} \tag{20.21}$$

we have

$$'\tilde{F}_1 = \tilde{F}_1 \tag{20.22}$$

since the contribution from the momentum increase in the interior drops out in the average as explained above. Since the flux of mass through $\mathcal{T}$ is zero, we have

$$\oint_{\mathcal{T}} \{(U^{\infty}+u_1)\,dy-u_2\,dx\} = 0$$

so that

$$'F_1 = -\oint_{\mathcal{T}} p\,dy - \oint_{\mathcal{T}} \rho u_1\{(u_1+U^{\infty})\,dy-u_2\,dx\} \qquad (20.23)$$

When observed from the body the flow is not steady so that we cannot use Bernoulli's law effectively to determine p. However, at distances far from the body the flow is steady when observed from the vortex street. The velocity when observed from the vortex street is clearly

$$U-U_R \qquad (20.24)$$

Thus using Bernoulli's law, cf. (2.7), for this steady flow we have

$$-p = \frac{\rho}{2}\{(u_1-U_R)^2+u_2^2\}-\frac{\rho}{2}U_R^2 \qquad (20.25)$$

supposing that $p = 0$ at infinity. Thus

$$-p = \frac{\rho}{2}\{u_1^2+u_2^2\}-\rho U_R u_1 \qquad (20.26)$$

Substituting the last relation in (20.23) we obtain

$$'F_1 = +\oint_{\mathcal{T}} [\rho\{u_1^2+u_2^2\}-\rho U_R u_1]\,dy$$
$$-\rho(u_1^2+u_1 U^{\infty})\,dy+\rho u_1 u_2\,dx \qquad (20.27)$$

or $\quad 'F_1 = \frac{\rho}{2}\int_{\mathcal{T}} \{(u_2^2-u_1^2)\,dy+2u_1 u_2\,dx\}-\rho U^T\int_{\mathcal{T}} u_1\,dy \qquad (20.28)$

where, of course, we use the relation, cf. (20.19),

$$U^{\infty}+U_R = U^T \qquad (20.29)$$

We now expand the box $\mathcal{T}$ first in the negative x_1-direction and then in the x_2-direction while we suppose that

$$|w| \sim \frac{C}{r}|W|^2-\frac{1}{r^2} \qquad \text{as } r \to \infty \qquad (20.30)$$

keeping the face $x = x_0$ fixed.

Accordingly, we obtain

$$'F_1 = \frac{\rho}{2} \int_{\mathscr{T}'} \{u_2^2 - u_1^2\} \, dy - \rho U^T \int_{x=x_0} u_1 \, dy \qquad (20.31)$$

where $\mathscr{T}'$ is the plane $x_1 = x_0$

$$u_2^2 - u_1^2 = -\operatorname{Re} \bar{w}^2 \qquad (20.32)$$

so that

$$(u_2^2 - u_1^2) \, dy = -\operatorname{Im} \bar{w}^2 \, dz \qquad (20.33)$$

when $dx = 0$.

Thus (20.31) becomes

$$'F_1 = -\frac{\rho}{2} \operatorname{Im} \int_{\substack{\mathscr{T} \\ x_1 = x_0}} (+\bar{w}^2 + 2U^T \bar{w}) \, dz \qquad (20.34)$$

As explained before, we shall suppose that in plane $x_1 = x_0$ the actual flow is the flow due to a full double vortex street as given by (20.11) and (20.13).

By a straightforward computation we can easily check

$$\frac{d}{dz} \frac{\sin \frac{\pi}{d} z}{\cos \frac{\pi}{d} \zeta - \cos \frac{\pi}{d} z} = -\frac{\pi}{d} \frac{\sin^2 \frac{\pi}{d} z}{\left[\cos \frac{\pi}{d} \zeta - \cos \frac{\pi}{d} z\right]^2} + \frac{\pi}{d} \frac{\cos \pi z}{\cos \frac{\pi}{d} \zeta - \cos \frac{\pi}{d} z};$$

collecting terms we get

$$\frac{d}{dz} \frac{\sin \frac{\pi}{d} z}{\cos \frac{\pi}{d} \zeta - \cos \frac{\pi}{d} z} = -\frac{\pi}{d} \frac{\cos \frac{\pi}{d} \zeta \cos \pi z - 1}{\left[\cos \frac{\pi}{d} \zeta - \cos \frac{\pi}{d} z\right]^2}$$

and adding and subtracting $\cos^2 (\pi/d)\zeta$ from the numerator of the last expression we obtain

$$\frac{d}{dz} \frac{\sin \frac{\pi}{d} z}{\cos \frac{\pi}{d} \zeta - \cos \frac{\pi}{d} z} = +\frac{\pi}{d} \left\{ \frac{\cos \frac{\pi}{d} \zeta}{\cos \frac{\pi}{d} \zeta - \cos \frac{\pi}{d} z} + \frac{\sin^2 \frac{\pi}{d} \zeta}{\left[\cos \frac{\pi}{d} \zeta - \cos \frac{\pi}{d} z\right]^2} \right\}$$

$$(20.35)$$

Thus using (20.13) and (20.16) we have

$$\frac{d}{dz}\frac{\sin\frac{\pi}{d}z}{\cos\frac{\pi}{d}\zeta-\cos\frac{\pi}{d}z} = -\frac{2d}{\gamma^2\pi}U_R\,\overline{w}(z)-\frac{d}{\gamma^2\pi}\overline{w}^2(z) \tag{20.36}$$

or

$$\frac{d}{dz}\left\{\frac{\pi\gamma^2}{d}\frac{\sin\frac{\pi}{d}z}{\cos\frac{\pi}{d}\zeta-\cos\frac{\pi}{d}z}+2(U_R+U^T)\chi\right\} = \overline{w}^2(z)+2U^T\overline{w} \tag{20.37}$$

where U_R is the velocity of the vortex street and U^T that of the body when observed from the vortex street. We can easily check

$$\lim_{y\to\pm\infty}\frac{\sin\frac{\pi(z-\zeta)}{2d}}{\sin\frac{\pi(z+\zeta)}{2d}} = e^{\pm i(\pi\zeta/d)} \tag{20.38}$$

so that (20.11) becomes

$$\chi(z)\to i\gamma\cdot\left(\pm i\frac{\pi\zeta}{d}\right) \qquad \text{as } y\to\pm\infty$$

or

$$\chi(z)\to \mp\gamma\frac{\pi\zeta}{d} \qquad \text{as } y\to\pm\infty \tag{20.39}$$

Thus using (20.34) and (20.37) we have

$$'F_1 = -\frac{\rho}{2}\mathrm{Im}\left\{\frac{\pi\gamma^2}{d}\frac{\sin\frac{\pi}{d}z}{\cos\frac{\pi}{d}\zeta-\cos\frac{\pi}{d}z}+2(U_R+U^T)\chi\right\}_{x_0-i\infty}^{x_0+i\infty} \tag{20.40}$$

and using (20.11), (20.38) and (20.39) we have

$$'F_1 = -\frac{\rho}{2}\mathrm{Im}\left\{\frac{2\pi\gamma^2}{di}+2(U_R+U^T)\cdot\left(-\frac{2\gamma\pi\zeta}{d}\right)\right\} \tag{20.41}$$

or

$$'F_1 = +\rho\frac{\pi\gamma^2}{d}+2\rho(U_R-U^T)\frac{\pi\gamma\rho}{d}\eta \tag{20.42}$$

Since $'F_1$ is independent of t we have that

$$\tilde{F}_1 = '\tilde{F}_1 = 'F_1$$

Furthermore, it should turn out as expected that $'F_1$ is positive. At first sight it would seem that it is remarkable that the force on a body in uniform motion through a fluid is independent of the shape of the body but a closer look at (20.42) will reveal that we do not know anything about the parameters γ, d and η and their dependence on the dimensions of the body. It should then follow that a closer look at the mode of generation of the vortex street will reveal that γ, d and η do depend on the shape of the body.

We proceed now to investigate *the stability of double vortex streets*. Given a physical model we can characterize its stability by perturbing it in all possible ways and then asking for the conditions under which this perturbation does not result in a complete change of the features of the model as $t \to \infty$ from what these features would have been had the model not been perturbed. These conditions then give us the conditions under which the model is stable. We consider only anti-symmetric vortex streets and will obtain a criterion for their stability.

We now perturb the position of the vortices given by (20.9) and (20.10) to

$$z_k^+ = \zeta + 2kd + \zeta_k^+, \qquad c = -2\pi\gamma \qquad (20.9)'$$

$$z_k = -\zeta + 2kd + \zeta_k^-, \qquad c = 2\pi\gamma \qquad (20.10)'$$

We may write the velocity potential for the system of vortices whose positions are given by (20.9)$'$ and (20.10)$'$ in the form

$$\chi(z) = i\gamma \sum_k \log(z - \zeta - 2kd - \zeta_k^+) - \log(z + \zeta - 2kd - \zeta_k^-) \qquad (20.43)$$

Differentiating the last expression with respect to z we obtain

$$\bar{w}(z) = i\gamma \sum_k \frac{1}{z - \zeta - 2kd - \zeta_k^+} - \frac{1}{z + \zeta - 2kd - \zeta_k^-} \qquad (20.44)$$

Accordingly, since

$$\dot{\zeta}_n^\pm + \dot{z}_n^\pm = \bar{w}_{\text{reg}}(\pm\zeta + 2nd + \zeta_n^\pm) \qquad (20.45)$$

where $\quad \dot{z}_n^\pm = i\gamma\left[\sum_k{}'\left(\frac{\pm 1}{2(n-k)d} \mp \frac{1}{\pm 2\zeta + 2(n-k)d}\right)\right] - i\gamma\frac{1}{2\zeta} \qquad (20.46)$

is the velocity of the unperturbed vortex street, we see that

$$\dot{\zeta}_n^\pm + \dot{z}_n^\pm = i\gamma \sum_k{}' \left(\frac{1}{\pm\zeta - \zeta + 2(n-k)d + \zeta_n^\pm - \zeta_k^+} \right.$$

$$\left. - \frac{1}{\pm\zeta + \zeta + 2(n-k)d + \zeta_n^\pm - \zeta_k^-} \right) \mp i\gamma \frac{1}{\pm 2\zeta + \zeta_n^\pm - \zeta_k^\mp}$$

Thus

$$\dot{\zeta}_n^\pm + \dot{z}_n^\pm = \pm i\gamma \sum_k{}' \left(\frac{1}{2(n-k)d + \zeta_n^\pm - \zeta_k^\pm} \right.$$

$$\left. - \frac{1}{\pm 2\zeta + 2(n-k)d + \zeta_n^\pm - \zeta_k^\pm} \right) \mp i\gamma \frac{1}{\pm 2\zeta + \zeta_n^\pm - \zeta_n^\mp} \tag{20.47}$$

Supposing that $(\zeta_n^\pm - \zeta_k^\mp) = o(1)$ and $(\zeta_n^\pm - \zeta_k^\pm) = o(1)$ we obtain from the last expression

$$\dot{\zeta}_n^\pm + \dot{z}_n^\pm = \pm i\gamma \left[\sum_k{}' \left(\frac{1}{2(n-k)d} - \frac{1}{\pm 2\zeta + (n-k)d} \right) \right] - \frac{i\gamma}{2\zeta}$$

$$\pm \frac{i\gamma}{4} \left(\sum_k \frac{\zeta_n^\pm - \zeta_n^\mp}{(\pm\zeta + (n-k)d)^2} - \sum_k{}' \frac{\zeta_n^\pm - \zeta_k^\pm}{(n-k)^2 d^2} \right)$$

so that using (20.46) we get

$$\dot{\zeta}_n^\pm = \pm \frac{i\gamma}{4} \left(\sum_k \frac{\zeta_n^\pm - \zeta_k^\mp}{(\pm\zeta + (n-k)d)^2} - \sum_k{}' \frac{\zeta_n^\pm - \zeta_k^\pm}{(n-k)^2 d^2} \right) \tag{20.48}$$

and

$$\dot{\zeta}_n^\pm = \mp \frac{i\gamma}{4} \left(\sum_k \frac{\dot{\zeta}_n^\pm - \dot{\zeta}_k^\mp}{(\pm\ +(n-k)d)^2} - \sum_k{}' \frac{\dot{\zeta}_n^\pm - \dot{\zeta}_k^\pm}{(n-k)^2 d^2} \right) \tag{20.49}$$

Introducing the variables

$$\zeta_n^\pm = {}^*\sigma^\pm e^{in\phi}, \qquad \zeta^\pm = \sigma^\pm e^{in\phi} \tag{20.50}$$

ϕ some fixed real number.

Equations (20.48) and (20.49) become

$${}^*\dot{\sigma}^\pm = \pm i \frac{\gamma}{4} \left(\sum_k \frac{\sigma^\pm - \sigma^\pm e^{-i(n-k)\phi}}{(\pm\zeta + (n-k)d)^2} - \sigma^\pm \sum_k{}' \frac{1 - e^{-i(n-k)\phi}}{(n-k)^2 d} \right) \tag{20.51}$$

$$\dot{\sigma}^\pm = \pm i \frac{\gamma}{4} \left(\sum_k {}^* \frac{\sigma^\pm - {}^*\sigma^\pm e^{-i(n-k)\phi}}{(\pm\zeta + (n-k)d)^2} - {}^*\sigma^\pm \sum_k{}' \frac{1 - e^{-i(n-k)\phi}}{(n-k)^2 d^2} \right) \tag{20.52}$$

we thus obtain

$$\pm i\dot\sigma^\pm = {}^*C^\pm {}^*\sigma^\pm + {}^*D^\mp {}^*\sigma^\mp \tag{20.53}$$

$$\mp i{}^*\dot\sigma^\pm = C^\pm \sigma^\pm + D^\mp \sigma^\mp \tag{20.54}$$

where $$D^\mp = -\frac{\gamma}{4}\sum_{k=-\infty}^{+\infty}\frac{e^{-i(n-k)\phi}}{(\pm\zeta+(n-k)d)^2} \tag{20.55}$$

$$C^\pm = \frac{\gamma}{4}\left(\sum_{k=-\infty}^{+\infty}\frac{1}{(\pm\zeta+(n-k)d)^2} - \sum_k{}'\frac{1-e^{-i(n-k)\phi}}{(n-k)^2\,d^2}\right) \tag{20.56}$$

$${}^*D^\mp = -\frac{\gamma}{4}\sum_{k=-\infty}^{+\infty}\frac{e^{-i(n-k)\phi}}{(\pm\bar\zeta+(n-k)d)^2} \tag{20.57}$$

$${}^*C^\pm = \frac{\gamma}{4}\left(\sum_{k=-\infty}^{+\infty}\frac{1}{(\pm\bar\zeta+(n-k)d)^2} - \sum_k{}'\frac{1-e^{-i(n-k)\phi}}{(n-k)^2\,d^2}\right) \tag{20.58}$$

In the case of an anti-symmetric vortex street which we are now considering $\zeta = \frac{1}{2}d + i\eta$ so that

$$D^\mp = {}^*D^\pm \tag{20.59}$$

$$C^\mp = {}^*C^\pm = C \tag{20.60}$$

since, as may be easily checked,

$$\sum_{k=-\infty}^{+\infty}\frac{e^{-i(n-k)\phi}}{(\pm\zeta+(n-k)d)^2} \tag{20.61}$$

is independent of n and $C^+ = C^-$.

Introducing the variable

$$r^\pm = {}^*\sigma^+ \pm \sigma^-, \qquad {}^*r^\pm = \sigma^+ \pm {}^*\sigma^- \tag{20.62}$$

equations (20.53), (20.54) become

$$i{}^*\dot r^\pm = C^- r^\pm + D^+ {}^*r^\pm \tag{20.63}$$

$$-i\dot r^\pm = C^+ {}^*r^\pm + D^- r^\pm \tag{20.64}$$

so that in the new variables the system (20.53), (20.54) of differential equations separates. The anti-symmetric vortex street can be stable only if the solutions of the system (20.63), (20.64) are bounded. Letting

$$r^\pm = R\,e^{i\lambda t}, \qquad {}^*r^\pm = R^*\,e^{i\lambda t} \tag{20.65}$$

we get $\qquad -\lambda R^* = C^- R + D^+ R^*, \qquad \lambda R = C^+ R^* + D^- R$

or $\qquad (D^+ + \lambda)R^* + C^- R = 0, \qquad C^+ R^* + (D^- - \lambda)R = 0$

The latter system of equations have a non-trivial solution if and only if

$$\begin{vmatrix} D^+ + \lambda & C^- \\ C^+ & D^- - \lambda \end{vmatrix} = 0$$

or, equivalently, if and only if

$$\lambda^2 - (D^- - D^+)\lambda - D^+ D^- + C^- C^+ = 0 \tag{20.66}$$

In order that the solutions to (20.63), (20.64) be bounded it is necessary that all roots λ of (20.66) be real.

The necessary and sufficient condition that all the roots of (20.66) be real is that

$$(D^- - D^+)^2 + 4(D^+ D^- - C^- C^+) \geqq 0$$

so that $\qquad\qquad (D^+ + D^-)^2 > 4C^+ C^- \tag{20.67}$

is the condition required for the stability of the anti-symmetric vortex street. Clearly since $C^+ = C^-$ the right hand side of the last relation is positive if we pick $\phi = \pi$ we can show that

$$D^+ = -D^-$$

so that $(D^+ + D^-) = 0$ and we obtain the condition

$$C^+ = 0 \tag{20.68}$$

This condition is a necessary condition for the stability of the anti-symmetric double vortex street.

However, we can easily see from (20.58) that $C^- = C^+$ is independent of n, and setting $n = 0$ in (20.58) we have that

$$C = \frac{\gamma}{4}\left(\sum_k \frac{1}{(-\zeta + (-k)d)^2} - {\sum_k}' \frac{1 - e^{-i(-k)\phi}}{(-k)^2 d^2} \right)$$

Since $\zeta = \tfrac{1}{2}d + i\eta$, we have

$$C^+ = \frac{\gamma}{4}\left(\sum_k \frac{1}{(+i\eta + (k+\tfrac{1}{2})d)^2} - 2\sum_{k=1}^{\infty} \frac{1 - \cos k\phi}{k^2 d^2} \right)$$

or
$$C^+ = \frac{\gamma}{4}\left(\sum_k \frac{-\eta^2 + (k+\tfrac{1}{2})^2 d^2}{[(k+\tfrac{1}{2})^2 d^2 + \eta^2]^2} - \frac{2}{d^2}\tfrac{1}{4}\phi(2\pi - \phi)\right) \tag{20.69}$$

The last relation is a consequence of the previous one as we may easily see from the following two equations.

$$\sum_k \frac{k+\tfrac{1}{2}}{[(k+\tfrac{1}{2})^2 d^2 + \eta^2]} = 0$$

and
$$\phi(2\pi - \phi) = \sum_{k=1}^{\infty} \frac{4}{k^2}(1 - \cos k\phi)$$

Furthermore, using the well-known formula

$$\frac{\pi^2}{d^2}\frac{1}{\cosh^2 \pi \dfrac{\eta}{d}} = \sum_k \frac{-\eta^2 + (k+\tfrac{1}{2})^2 d^2}{[(k+\tfrac{1}{2})^2 d^2 + \eta^2]^2}$$

we obtain

$$C^+ = \frac{\gamma}{4}\left(\frac{\pi^2}{d^2}\frac{1}{\cosh^2 \pi \dfrac{\eta}{d}} - \frac{\phi(2\pi - \phi)}{2d^2}\right) \tag{20.70}$$

Setting $\phi = \pi$ (20.70) becomes

$$C^+ = \frac{\gamma}{4}\frac{\pi^2}{d^2}\left(\frac{1}{\cosh^2 \pi \dfrac{\eta}{d}} - \frac{1}{2}\right)$$

Thus the necessary condition for stability of the anti-symmetric double vortex street (20.68) leads to the condition that

$$\cosh \pi \frac{\eta}{d} = \sqrt{2}$$

or
$$\pi \frac{\eta}{d} = \cdot 8814$$

whence
$$\frac{\eta}{d} = \cdot 281 \tag{20.71}$$

It is remarkable that the actual anti-symmetric vortex streets observed in nature satisfy a condition very close to (20.71).

CHAPTER 21

Viscous Fluid Flows

In this chapter we shall be concerned with the problem of describing the solutions of the system of partial differential equations governing viscous fluid flows known as the Navier-Stokes equations. Viscosity produces stresses in the fluid in addition to the pressure. Due to these stresses a force, in addition to the pressure force, acts on a unit volume.

More specifically[1] there exists a stress tensor $\tau = (\tau_{ik}) = \{\tau_{ki}\}$ representing the stresses on the fluid due to the viscosity of the fluid and the pressure distribution along the field of flow. In the case of parallel flow given by $u_1 = u(x_2) u_2 = u_3 = 0$ the part of the stress tensor due to the viscosity is

$$\tau_{21} = \tau_{12} = \mu \nabla_2 u_1$$

while all other components are zero. The coefficient μ is a constant called the viscosity. In general,

$$\tau_{ik} = \mu(\nabla_i u_k + \nabla_k u_i)$$

It follows that the force due to viscosity and pressure exerted per unit volume is given by the divergence of τ,

$$F = \nabla(\tau)$$

i.e. $$F_i = \{\nabla_1 \tau_{1i} + \nabla_2 \tau_{2i} + \nabla_3 \tau_{3i}\}$$

Specifically, because of $(\nabla u) = 0$,

$$\nabla(\tau) = -\nabla p + \mu \nabla^2 u$$

Accordingly, the equation of conservation of momentum takes the form

$$\rho\{\nabla_t u + (u\nabla)u\} = -\nabla p + \mu \nabla^2 u \qquad (21.1)$$

[1] Cf. von Mises and Friedrichs: *Lecture notes on Fluid Dynamics*, Brown University, 1942, Chapter IV, p. 141.

and the equation describing the conservation of mass

$$(\nabla u) = 0 \tag{21.2}$$

remains unchanged.

The system of partial differential equations (21.1) and (21.2) is known as the *Navier-Stokes* equations for incompressible viscous fluid flow.

We consider flows of a fluid with obstacles for which the velocity at infinity is prescribed. The question now arises as to what are the appropriate boundary conditions to be imposed in a given problem in order to make the solution of (21.1) and (21.2) unique. It has been found that a reasonable boundary condition in a viscous fluid flow is that the velocity u vanish on the surface of the bodies: i.e. all three components should vanish and not only the tangential components as

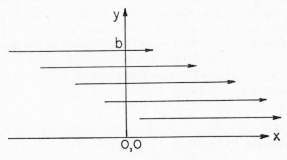

Fig. 21.1.   Couette flow.

in potential flow. There exist two simple solutions of equation (21.1) and (21.2). The first describes the "Couette flow", the two-dimensional shear flow between a fixed plate given by the plane $y = 0$ and a plate moving with velocity $\{u, 0, 0\}$ given by the plane $y = b$, see Fig 21.1. Clearly since $v = 0$ and since u is independent of x we see from (21.1) that

$$-\mu\Delta u + \nabla_x p = 0$$

$$+\nabla_y p = 0$$

Accordingly we see that $p \equiv$ const. and that u satisfies the differential equation

$$\frac{d^2 u}{dy^2} = 0$$

with the boundary conditions

$$u = 0 \qquad y = 0$$
$$u = U \qquad y = b$$

Consequently,
$$u = U\frac{y}{b}$$

The second flow known as the "Poiseuille flow" is the shear flow between two fixed plates $y = \pm b$. In this case we clearly get the same differential equations

$$-\mu\Delta u + \nabla_x p = 0$$

$$\nabla_y p = 0 \tag{21.3}$$

where we require that u be independent of x. Accordingly we see that p is independent of y and from (21.3) we have

$$\mu\frac{d^2 u}{dy^2} = +\rho\nabla_x p \tag{21.4}$$

Since in the latter equation the left hand side depends only on y while the right hand side depends only on x it follows that both sides are equal to a constant

$$\mu\frac{d^2 u}{dy^2} = -\frac{2U}{b^2}$$

The flow is then given by

$$u = U\left(1 - \frac{y^2}{b^2}\right), \qquad v = 0$$

$$p = -\frac{2xU}{b^2} + p_0$$

This flow can be easily checked to satisfy the differential equations above.

In looking for solutions of the Navier-Stokes equations there are in particular two possible approximations we can make. One approximation can be made when the viscosity μ is large in which case the term $(u\nabla)u$ in (21.1) is disregarded in the first approximation and then an iteration procedure of the form

$$\rho\{\nabla_t u_i + (u\nabla)u_i\} = -\nabla p + \mu\nabla^2 u_{i-1}$$

may be used. The other approximation is to be made when μ is small. We shall concern ourselves only with the latter case.

Before proceeding further, however, we shall consider the *similarity* of viscous fluid flows, i.e. solutions of the Navier-Stokes equations.

Suppose that we have solved a given flow problem involving the Navier-Stokes equations. We then ask whether we have at the same time solved "similar" flow problems involving the Navier-Stokes equations. To answer this question we stretch the dimensions by a factor and the data by another factor to obtain a new flow problem. We then try to find the conditions under which the solution of one problem is transformed into the solution of the new problem.

Consider a flow problem $\mathscr{P}$ with data $\mathscr{D}$ involving a domain D with boundary $\mathscr{B}$ with entrance and exit E. On $\mathscr{B}$ the velocity $u = 0$, while on E the velocity $u = U_E$ is prescribed so that

$$\int_E U_E \cdot n \, dE = 0 \tag{21.5}$$

We prescribe further both ρ and μ. Consider a similar problem $\mathscr{P}'$ having similar data $\mathscr{D}'$. Suppose that

(1) there is a similarity mapping $x' = \alpha x$ with α constant such that B', E' is the image of B, E.

(2) in addition, there is a constant β such that the velocities prescribed at E' are

$$U'_{E'} = \beta U_E \tag{21.6}$$

(3) ρ', μ' are constants to be left open.

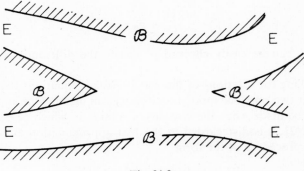

Fig. 21.2.

We then say that the flow resulting from problem $\mathscr{P}'$ is *similar* to the flow resulting from $\mathscr{P}$ if u' at corresponding points $x' = \alpha x$ is exactly $u' = \beta u$. The similarity of the two flows depends on ρ', u', ρ and u. To find the necessary conditions for similarity we select a significant length L, and a velocity U defined by the data and then we introduce the dimensionless quantities

$$\frac{x}{L}, \quad \frac{tU}{L}, \quad \frac{u}{U} \tag{21.7}$$

The two flows are said to be kinematically similar if

$$\frac{x'}{L'} = \frac{x}{L}, ..., \frac{u'}{U'} = \frac{u}{U} \tag{21.8}$$

In terms of the dimensionless variables (21.7) the Navier-Stokes equations take the form

$$U^{-2}L\nabla_t u + U^{-2}L(U\nabla)u = -U^{-2}L\rho^{-1}\nabla p + U^{-2}L\rho^{-1}\mu\nabla^2 u \tag{21.9}$$

$$U'^{-2}L'\nabla_t u' + U'^{-2}L'(u'\nabla)u' = -U'^{-2}L'\rho'^{-1}\nabla p' + U'^{-2}L'\rho'^{-1}\mu'\nabla^2 u' \tag{21.10}$$

if the two flows resulting from problems $\mathscr{P}$, $\mathscr{P}'$ are similar the left members of (21.9) and (21.10) are the same as can be easily seen from (21.8). Consequently the similar flow is a solution of the similar problem if members of the right hand sides of (21.9) and (21.10) are equal. We thus obtain the conditions

$$\frac{p'}{\rho'U'^2} = \frac{p}{\rho U^2} \tag{21.11}$$

and

$$\frac{\mu'}{\rho'U'L'} = \frac{\mu}{\rho UL} \tag{21.12}$$

We now define the Reynolds number

$$R = \frac{\rho UL}{\mu} = \frac{UL}{\nu} \tag{21.13}$$

using the kinematic viscosity $\nu = \mu/\rho$. We thus see that the condition for the two flow problems $\mathscr{P}$ and $\mathscr{P}'$ to have similar solutions is that they have the same value of R. The pressure is uniquely determined up to an additive constant so that

$$\frac{p'}{\rho' U'^2} = \frac{2}{\rho U^2}$$

can always be satisfied.

CHAPTER 22

Boundary Layer Theory

We now consider the theory of *viscous flow for large Reynolds numbers,* or equivalently for $\mu \to 0$. We shall be interested in the behavior of the flow close to a body present in the fluid. In particular we consider the two-dimensional steady flow past a plate. We suppose that the flow is in the (x, y) plane with the profile of the plate given by the two functions

$$y^{\pm} = -a \pm y(x), \qquad x \geqq 0 \tag{22.1}$$

with
$$y(0) = 0$$

and
$$y(x) = a, \qquad x \geqq x_0$$

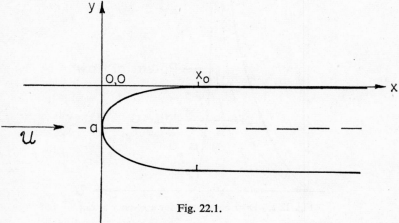

Fig. 22.1.

Let $\vec{u} = (u, v)$, then the Navier-Stokes equations take the form

$$(\nabla \vec{u}) = 0 \tag{22.2}$$

$$\rho(\vec{u} \nabla) \vec{u} = -\nabla p - \mu \nabla^2 \vec{u} \tag{22.3}$$

153

with the boundary conditions

$$u = 0, \qquad v = 0 \quad \text{on } B$$

and $\qquad u = U, \qquad v = 0 \quad \text{at } \infty, \qquad U > 0$

In the limit as $\mu \to 0$ we shall assume that we get the potential flow past the plate $\overset{o}{u}(x)$, $\overset{o}{v}(x)$. This flow, however, violates the condition that $(\overset{o}{\vec{u}} \cdot \tan) = 0$ on B, although it satisfies the condition that $(\vec{u} \cdot n) = 0$ along the surface of the body. This indicates that for small viscosity there is a very narrow layer in which the velocity will have a value differing very much from the limit flow. This layer is called the *boundary layer*, see Fig. 22.2. We set

$$\overset{o}{u}(x, 0) = \overset{o}{U}(x) \tag{22.4}$$

Upon using Bernoulli's law and supposing that $\overset{o}{p} = 0$ at infinity we have

$$\overset{o}{p}(x, 0) = \overset{o}{p}(x) = -\frac{\rho}{2}[\overset{o}{U}^2(x) - U^2] \tag{22.5}$$

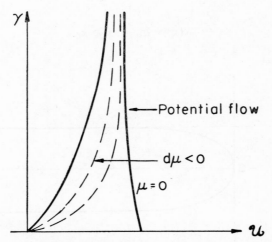

Fig. 22.2. Distribution of u for a given $x > x_0$.

We now introduce a *second limit process*. For this purpose we introduce the new variables

$$x, \qquad \eta = \frac{y}{\delta} \tag{22.6}$$

$$u, \qquad \omega = \frac{v}{\delta} \qquad (22.7)$$

$$\mu\rho^{-1} = v, \qquad p' = \frac{p}{\rho} \qquad (22.8)$$

The Navier-Stokes equations then become

$$\nabla_x u + \nabla_\eta \omega = 0 \qquad (22.9)$$

$$u\nabla_x u + \omega\nabla_\eta u = -\nabla_x p' + v\nabla_x^2 u + v\delta^{-2}\nabla_\eta^2 u \qquad (22.10)$$

$$\delta^2[u\nabla_x \omega + \omega\nabla_\eta \omega] = -\nabla_\eta p' + \delta^2[\gamma\nabla_x^2 \omega + v\delta^{-2}\nabla_\eta^2 \omega] \qquad (22.11)$$

Let $\delta = v^{\frac{1}{2}}\sigma^{-1}$ with σ constant. In the limit, as $v \to 0$, the Navier-Stokes equations then become

$$\nabla_x u + \nabla_\eta \omega = 0 \qquad (22.12)$$

$$u\nabla_x u + \omega\nabla_\eta u = -\nabla_x p' + \sigma^2\nabla_\eta^2 u \qquad (22.13)$$

$$\nabla_\eta p' = 0 \qquad (22.14)$$

The boundary conditions at the wall for (22.12), (22.13), (22.14) should be $u = \omega = 0$. We disregard at the present the boundary conditions for $|x| \to \infty$.

Before proceeding further we look at the situation for the simple case where the differential equation is

$$a - f_y = vf_{yy}, \qquad a > 0, \qquad v > 0$$

and the boundary conditions are

$$f(0) = 0, \qquad f(1) = 1$$

The solution of this differential equation satisfying the boundary conditions is

$$f = ay + \frac{(1 - e^{-y/v})}{1 - e^{-1/v}}(1 - a)$$

as $v \to 0^+$ we see that

$$f \to \overset{\circ}{f} = ay + (1 - a)$$

so that the boundary condition is kept at 1 whereas the boundary condition is lost at $y = 0$.

To examine this situation more closely we make the change of variables

$$\eta = \frac{y}{v};$$

our differential equation becomes

$$av - f_\eta = f_{\eta\eta}, \qquad 0 \leqq \eta \leqq 1/v$$

with $\qquad f(1/v) = 1 \quad \text{and} \quad f(0) = 0$

When we let $v \to 0$ the function $f(\eta)$ will approach a function $F(\eta)$ defined for $0 < \eta < \infty$ which satisfies the differential equation

$$_{\eta\eta} + f_\eta = 0, \qquad 0 \leqq \eta \leqq \infty$$

with the boundary condition

$$f(0) = 0$$

The boundary condition to be imposed at infinity must now be determined. Clearly

$$f(\eta) = av\eta + \frac{(1 - e^{-\eta})}{1 - e^{-1/v}}(1 - a)$$

letting $v \to 0$ first and then letting $\eta \to \infty$ we find that

$$F(\eta) = (1 - e^{-\eta})(1 - a)$$

as $\eta \to 0$ $\qquad\qquad F(\eta) \to 0$

whereas as $\eta \to \infty$ $\qquad\quad F(\eta) \to (1 - a)$

which is $\qquad\qquad \lim_{y \to 0}\left(\lim_{v \to 0} f(y)\right) = (1 - a)$

We thus keep the boundary condition at $y = 0$ whereas at $\eta = \infty$ we impose the boundary condition of the limit problem as $v \to 0$ at $y = 0$. The important feature of the boundary layer theory is then that the boundary condition for $\eta \to \infty$ is not the boundary condition for original flow as $y \to 0$ but, instead,

$$u \to \overset{o}{u}(x) \qquad\qquad\qquad (22.15)$$

We need not impose conditions on ω as $\eta \to \infty$ since for each $\delta > 0$, $v = \delta\omega = 0$ as $\eta \to \infty$. But we must require

$$p \to \overset{o}{p}(x) \quad \text{as } v \to 0 \tag{22.16}$$

As a consequence of (22.14) we then have

$$p = \overset{o}{p}(x) \text{ throughout.} \tag{22.17}$$

It is convenient to re-introduce the old variables for fixed v and a fixed value of x. Thus we obtain the problem

$$\nabla_x u + \nabla_y v = 0 \tag{22.18}$$

$$u\nabla_x u + v\nabla_y u = -\nabla_x \overset{o}{p}' + v\nabla_y^2 u \tag{22.19}$$

$$u = v = 0 \quad \text{at } y = 0 \tag{22.20}$$

$$u = \overset{o}{u}(x) \quad \text{as } y \to \infty \tag{22.21}$$

We consider as a typical example the problem of the flow past a *flat plate*, i.e. a plate lying on $y = 0$ for $x \geqq 0$ and thus having thickness zero. The conditions for the flow are then

$$y^{\pm}(x) = 0 \tag{22.22}$$

In this case the main flow is given by

$$\overset{o}{u}(x) = U = \text{const.} \tag{22.23}$$

$$\overset{o}{p}(x) = \overset{o}{p} = \text{const.} \tag{22.24}$$

$$u(x) = U, \quad x \leqq 0 \tag{22.25}$$

This problem can be explicitly reduced to a solution of an ordinary differential equation. For this purpose we introduce the variable

$$\tau = \frac{y}{\sqrt{(vx/U)}} \tag{22.26}$$

and set $\qquad\qquad u = Uf'(\tau) \tag{22.27}$

so that $\qquad\qquad \psi = \sqrt{(Uvx)}f(\tau) \tag{22.28}$

Since $v = -\partial\psi/\partial x$ we have

$$v = \frac{1}{2}\sqrt{\left(\frac{Uv}{x}\right)}\left[\tau f'(\tau) - f(\tau)\right] \tag{22.29}$$

Thus

$$uu_x + vu_y = -\frac{1}{2}\frac{U^2}{x}\left[\tau f'(\tau) - \tau f'(\tau) + f(\tau)\right]f''(\tau) \tag{22.30}$$

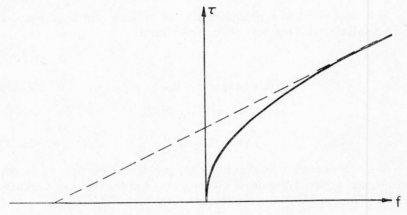

Fig. 22.3.

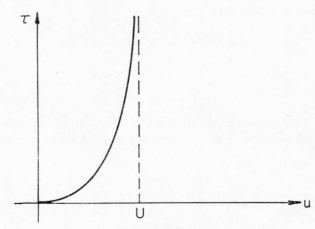

Fig. 22.4.

Furthermore, since

$$\nabla_y^2 u = \frac{U^2}{\nu x} f'''(\tau) \tag{22.31}$$

we obtain from (22.19) and (22.30) the differential equation which $f(\tau)$ is to satisfy,

$$2f'''(\tau) = -f(\tau)f''(\tau) \tag{22.32}$$

together with the boundary conditions

$$f(0) = f'(0) = 0, \qquad f'(\infty) = 1$$

Noting that $v \to 0$ as $y \to \infty$ we have from (22.26) that $v \to 0$ as $\tau \to \infty$ so that using (22.29) we obtain that

$$f(\tau) \sim \tau f'(\tau) \quad \text{as } \tau \to \infty$$

There are various numerical methods which can be used to integrate (22.32). An existence proof was given by Weyl in 1942. (Weyl, H.: "On the differential equations of the simplest boundary-layer problems." *Annals af Mathematics*, vol. 43, No. 2, April 1942, pp. 381–407.)

We now define the quantity

$$\tau_{xy} = \mu \nabla_y u \, |^{y=0}$$

as the skin friction resistance and

$$D(x) = \mu \int_0^x \nabla_y u(x, 0) \, dx$$

as the skin friction drag. In this case the skin friction resistance becomes

$$\tau_{xy} = \rho U^2 \sqrt{\left(\frac{\nu}{Ux}\right)} f''(0)$$

and the skin drag becomes

$$D(x) = 2\rho U^2 \sqrt{\left(\frac{\nu x}{U}\right)} f''(0)$$

From (22.32) we note that

$$f(0) = f'(0) = f^{(3)}(0) = f^{(4)}(0) = 0$$
$$2f^{(5)}(0) = -[f''(0)]^2 = -\beta^2$$

thus
$$f(\lambda) = \frac{\beta\lambda^2}{2!} - \frac{\beta^2\lambda^5}{2\cdot 5!}$$

$$f'(\lambda) = \beta\lambda - \frac{\beta^2\lambda^4}{2\cdot 4!}$$

$$f''(\lambda) = \beta - \frac{\beta^2\lambda^3}{2\cdot 3!}$$

We now determine β and λ_0 so that
$$f''(\lambda_0) = 0 \quad \text{and} \quad f'(\lambda_0) = 1$$

Upon solving the resulting system of two equations in the unknowns β and λ_0 we obtain approximately
$$f''(0) = \beta = \frac{4}{9} = \cdot 444...$$

$$\lambda_0 = 3$$

Even though we get such a large value of λ_0 the result is in good comparison with the "exact" value for $f''(0)$
$$f''(0) = \cdot 33$$

It is convenient to define the displacement thickness δ_1 by
$$\delta_1 = U^{-1}\int_0^\infty (U-u)\,dy = \int_0^\infty [1-f'(\tau)]\,dy$$

so that
$$\delta_1 = \sqrt{\left(\frac{vx}{U}\right)}\int_0^\infty [1-f'(\tau)]\,d\tau = \eta\sqrt{\left(\frac{vx}{U}\right)}$$

The displacement thickness is in some respects a measure of the thickness of the boundary layer.

We have so far carried out an approximation of first order in the boundary layer. As we shall see below it is a very simple matter to give a refinement of the free stream flow. For this purpose consider an expansion of u, v, p considered as function of x and y in terms of some parameter
$$u(x, y) = \overset{0}{u}(x, y) + \overset{1}{u}(x, y) + ...$$

$$v(x, y) = \overset{0}{v}(x, y) + \overset{1}{v}(x, y) + ...$$

$$p(x, y) = \overset{0}{p}(x, y) + \overset{1}{p}(x, y) + ...$$

The terms $\overset{1}{u}, \overset{1}{v}, \overset{1}{p}$ are proportional to an approximate power of v. We shall see that these terms are of order $\sqrt{v}$. The Navier-Stokes equations become up to terms of first order

$$\nabla_x \overset{1}{u} + \nabla_y \overset{1}{v} = 0$$

$$\rho \overset{0}{u} \nabla_x \overset{1}{u} + \nabla_x \overset{1}{p} = 0$$

$$\rho \overset{0}{u} \nabla_x \overset{1}{v} + \nabla_y \overset{1}{p} = 0$$

$$B.C. \text{ at } \infty \qquad \overset{1}{u} = \overset{1}{v} = 0$$

The important feature of the present problem is that at the wall, $y = 0$, the condition

$$\overset{1}{v}(x, 0) = v(x, \infty)$$

should be imposed, where $v(x, y)$ is the v-component of the boundary layer flow. Since for the flat plate

$$v(x, \infty) = \tfrac{1}{2}\eta \sqrt{\left(\frac{Uv}{x}\right)}$$

is of order $\sqrt{v}$ the same is true of $\overset{1}{v}(x, 0)$, thus $\overset{1}{v}(x, y)$, $\overset{1}{u}(x, y)$, $\overset{1}{p}(x, y)$ are of order $\sqrt{v}$. In the case $\overset{0}{u}(x, y) = U = \text{const.}$ we have

$$\nabla_x (\nabla_y \overset{1}{u} - \nabla_x \overset{1}{v}) = 0$$

$$\nabla_y \overset{1}{u} - \nabla_x \overset{1}{v} = 0$$

and $(\overset{1}{u}, \overset{1}{v})$ is a potential flow.

For the flat plate

$$\overset{1}{u} - i\overset{1}{v} = -\tfrac{1}{2}\eta \sqrt{\left(\frac{Uv}{x + iy}\right)}$$

Setting $x^2 + y^2 = r^2$

$$\frac{x - iy}{r} = e^{-i\theta}$$

then $\sqrt{\left(\dfrac{x-iy}{r}\right)} = e^{-i\theta/2} = \cos\dfrac{\theta}{2} - i\sin\dfrac{\theta}{2} = \sqrt{\left(\dfrac{1+x/r}{2}\right)} - i\sqrt{\left(\dfrac{1-x/r}{2}\right)}$

so that $\sqrt{(x-iy)} = \sqrt{\left(\dfrac{r+x}{2}\right)} - i\sqrt{\left(\dfrac{r-x}{2}\right)}$

Accordingly, $\overset{1}{u} - i\overset{1}{v} = -\dfrac{i}{2r}\eta\sqrt{(Uv)}\sqrt{(x-iy)}$

so that $\overset{1}{u} = -\dfrac{\eta\sqrt{(Uv)}}{2r}\sqrt{\left(\dfrac{r-x}{2}\right)}$

$\overset{1}{v} = +\dfrac{\eta\sqrt{(Uv)}}{2r}\sqrt{\left(\dfrac{r+x}{2}\right)}$

Thus $u(x,y) + \overset{1}{u}(x,y) = Uf'\left(y\sqrt{\dfrac{U}{vx}}\right) - \dfrac{\eta\sqrt{(Uv)}}{2}\sqrt{\left(\dfrac{r-x}{2}\right)}$

Accordingly we see that there is a reduction in speed in the main stream due to the thickening of the boundary layer.

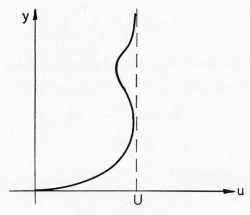

Fig. 22.5.

CHAPTER 23

Instability of Discontinuity Surface

Various flows that are solutions of the Navier-Stokes equations do not occur since they are unstable. These flows eventually change into unsteady flows. For example, the flow around a cylinder gives rise to a vortex pair on the rear side, which, if R exceeds a certain value, will become unstable, break away and form an unsymmetrical Karmán vortex street. Under other circumstances the flow will change over into a completely irregular "turbulent" flow.

The first question we ask is when and under what circumstances is a given flow unstable. We call a flow unstable if after a slight disturbance the flow will not return to its original form. One expects that viscosity acts as a stabilizing factor by damping out any disturbances. Accordingly one would expect that instability of the above flows must already be revealed when the viscosity is disregarded. We shall discuss below whether or not this expectation is justified.

Flows of non-viscous fluids need not be irrotational. Since an irrotational flow is indifferent with respect to irrotational disturbances one should admit vorticity from the outset for instability investigations.

The simplest classical stability of a discontinuity surface of a flow with vorticity is the flow with a "free" surface. In two-dimensional flow such a surface is given by a line with the flow velocity different on both sides.

Let such a two-dimensional flow be given by the potential

$$\begin{aligned} \Phi = U_+ x, \quad & u = U_+, \quad v = 0, \quad y > 0 \\ = U_- x, \quad & u = U_-, \quad v = 0, \quad y < 0 \end{aligned} \tag{23.1}$$

The line $y = 0$ is then a discontinuity line. The pressure p and the density ρ are assumed to be different on both sides, i.e.

$$p = p_+, \qquad \rho = \rho_+, \qquad y > 0$$
$$p = p_-, \qquad \rho = \rho_-, \qquad y < 0 \tag{23.2}$$

The pressure p need not, of course, be constant and is a continuous function of position.

We assume that the flow is irrotational on both sides and we do not neglect gravity. We shall consider only perturbations in the position of the discontinuity line. We may simplify the problem by observing the

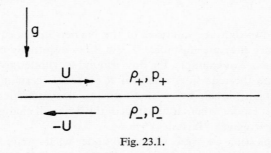

Fig. 23.1.

motion from a system moving with the velocity $\frac{1}{2}(U_+ + U_-)$. We set $U = \frac{1}{2}(U_+ - U_-)$. With reference to this system we then have

$$u = U, \qquad v = 0, \qquad y > 0$$
$$u = -U, \qquad v = 0, \qquad y < 0 \tag{23.3}$$

As a preliminary rough consideration suppose that the discontinuity line is distorted into the form of a wave. Then one might say that the velocity of the upper fluid is greater at a crest than at a trough and,

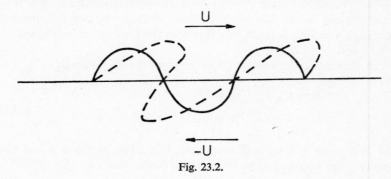

Fig. 23.2.

therefore, the crest will tip forward while the trough falls back. The same argument for the lower fluid yields a tendency in the same direction. This problem can be handled more carefully.

Suppose now that ϕ is the potential for the flow in excess of the parallel flow

$$\phi = \phi_+$$
$$\phi = \phi_- \tag{23.4}$$

We can then write Bernoulli's equation for non-steady irrotational flow, cf. (2.7), in the form

$$\nabla_t \phi_\pm + \tfrac{1}{2} |u \pm U|^2 + \frac{p_\pm}{\rho_\pm} + gy = c(t) \tag{23.5}$$

Since we can add to the potential ϕ any arbitrary function of t we can make the constant $c(t)$ in (23.5) equal to $\tfrac{1}{2}U^2$. We now assume that the deviations from the undisturbed flow are so small that terms of second order can be neglected; we shall see later the consequence of this assumption. Accordingly, Bernoulli's equation then becomes

$$\nabla_t \phi_\pm + \tfrac{1}{2}U^2 \pm Uu + p_\pm \rho_\pm^{-1} + gy = \tfrac{1}{2}U^2 \tag{23.6}$$

We represent the discontinuity surface by the function

$$y = \eta(t, x) \tag{23.7}$$

The condition of sliding along the surface leads to the condition that

$$v_\pm = \frac{\partial \eta}{\partial t} \pm U \frac{d\eta}{dx} \tag{23.8}$$

for $y = 0$.

We now consider equation (23.6) along the two sides of the discontinuity surface $y = \eta(t, x)$ and write down the difference of these two equations obtaining

$$\widehat{\rho\nabla_t \phi} + 2\widetilde{Uu\rho} + \hat{\rho}g\eta = 0 \tag{23.9}$$

Relations (23.8) and (23.9) must hold on the undisturbed discontinuity line, i.e. when $y = 0$.

We now perturb the discontinuity surface $y = 0$ to some surface

$$y = \eta(0, x) \tag{23.10}$$

at time $t = 0$ and consider the flow to be stable if, for no initial perturba tion, the disturbance which results in time grows indefinitely. We speak of instability if, for some initial perturbation, the resulting disturbance grows indefinitely. Any perturbation (23.10) among a sufficiently general class of perturbations may be either developed in a Fourier series or represented by a Fourier integral. Accordingly, it is sufficient to investigate perturbations of the form

$$\eta(0, x) = \eta_0 \, e^{i\alpha x} \tag{23.11}$$

where α is real. We suppose that we can obtain solutions $\eta(t, x)$ in the form

$$\eta(t, x) = \eta_0 \, e^{\beta t} \, e^{i\alpha x} \tag{23.12}$$

with β complex. Should we be able to find solutions of the form (23.12) with $\mathrm{Re}\,\beta > 0$ we then say that the flow is unstable. Otherwise the flow is stable.

We shall require that

$$\phi, \nabla_x \phi, \nabla_y \phi, \to 0 \quad \text{as } |y| \to \infty \tag{23.13}$$

We shall furthermore assume the form

$$\phi_{\pm}(x, y, t) = a_{\pm} e^{\beta t} e^{i\alpha x} e^{\mp |\alpha| y} \tag{23.14}$$

for the velocity potential.

Substituting (23.14) and (23.12) in the condition of sliding (23.8) we obtain

$$\beta \eta_0 \pm i U \eta_0 \alpha \pm |\alpha| a_{\pm} = 0 \tag{23.15}$$

whence

$$2\beta \eta_0 = -|\alpha| \hat{a}$$
$$i U \eta_0 \alpha = -|\alpha| \tilde{a} \tag{23.16}$$

From condition (23.9) we obtain upon substitution of (23.12) and (23.14)

$$\beta \widehat{\rho a} + 2 i U \alpha \widetilde{\rho a} + \eta_0 \, \hat{\rho} g = 0 \tag{23.17}$$

Since, as can be easily checked

$$\widehat{\rho a} = \hat{\rho} \tilde{a} + \tilde{\rho} \hat{a}$$
$$\widetilde{\rho a} = \tilde{\rho} \tilde{a} + \tfrac{1}{4} \hat{\rho} \hat{a} \tag{23.18}$$

we obtain using (23.16)

$$-|\alpha|\,\widehat{\rho a} = [\hat{\rho} i U \eta_0 \alpha + 2\tilde{\rho}\beta\eta_0]$$
$$-|\alpha|\,\widetilde{\rho a} = [\tilde{\rho} i U \eta_0 \alpha + \tfrac{1}{2}\hat{\rho}\beta\eta_0] \tag{23.19}$$

Substituting (23.19) in (23.17) we arrive at the quadratic equation for β

$$\beta[\hat{\rho} i U \alpha + 2\tilde{\rho}\beta] + 2iU\alpha[\tilde{\rho} i U \alpha + \tfrac{1}{2}\hat{\rho}\beta] - \hat{\rho}g\,|\alpha| = 0$$

or

$$2\tilde{\rho}\beta^2 + 2iU\alpha\hat{\rho}\beta - 2U^2\alpha^2\tilde{\rho} - g\,|\alpha|\,\hat{\rho} = 0$$

whence $\quad \beta = \dfrac{-2iU\alpha\hat{\rho} \pm \sqrt{(-4U^2\alpha^2\hat{\rho}^2 + 8\tilde{\rho}[2U^2\alpha^2\tilde{\rho} + g\,|\alpha|\,\hat{\rho}])}}{4\tilde{\rho}}$ (23.20)

In order for the undisturbed flow to be stable the argument of the square root in (23.20) must be negative or zero, i.e.

$$(4\tilde{\rho}^2 - \hat{\rho}^2)U^2\alpha^2 + 2g\,|\alpha|\,\hat{\rho}\tilde{\rho} \leqq 0 \tag{23.21}$$

Since $\qquad 4\tilde{\rho}^2 - \hat{\rho}^2 = 4\rho_+\rho_-$

our condition (23.21) for stability becomes

$$\rho_+\rho_- \leqq -\frac{g\hat{\rho}\tilde{\rho}}{2\,|\alpha|\,U^2} \tag{23.22}$$

Since $g > 0$, this condition for stability requires that the density of the upper fluid be much smaller than the density of the lower fluid. From the above result we can draw some very significant conclusions. For example, we can see that stable water waves of short wavelength are possible and that water waves are not stable if the wind velocity is too great or the wavelength too large.

Should α be small, stability can be assured although for α large we cannot assure stability. Accordingly, in a given flow problem involving a discontinuity surface a value of α can always be found for which

$$\text{Re } \beta > 0$$

so that these flows are not stable.

CHAPTER 24

Stability of Shear Flow

We note that in the previous chapter we have not taken viscosity into account and that viscosity is relatively effective for motions with large values of α so that we cannot parallel the above results for viscous fluid flows.

The problem of stability is in many respects quite different if the fluid is viscous. If the viscosity is large the flow is generally stable. For low viscosity, however, the flow may become unstable.

The lowest value of the Reynolds number for which this happens is called the *critical Reynolds number*. Such critical values have been calculated for only a few problems. One of the outstanding investigations of such initial values is given in G. I. Taylor's theory of rotating Couette flows where the theoretical value obtained checks well with experiment.

As mentioned before, one would expect that the presence of viscosity generally damps out any small disturbances of the flow and, therefore, if the flow of a perfect fluid is stable we would expect it to remain stable when the viscosity of the fluid is taken into account. However, it has been found that the exact opposite occurs for certain flows, i.e. the flow is unstable for certain values of the viscosity while it is stable again for larger values of the viscosity.

We shall describe the problem of the stability of a certain type of steady two-dimensional viscous fluid flow. Such a flow is described by a stream function $\psi(x, y)$ which satisfies the Navier-Stokes equation

$$U\Delta\Psi_x + V\Delta\Psi_y = \nu\Delta\Delta\Psi \qquad (24.1)$$

as can be derived by inserting ψ into the Navier-Stokes equations for two-dimensional flow and taking the curl.

Let $\Psi(x, y) + \psi(x, y, t)$ represent the unsteady flow resulting from a slight disturbance; hence, assume that ψ, $\Delta\psi$, $\Delta\Delta\psi$ are relatively small

169

so that it is sufficient to consider only terms of first order in ψ. Accordingly, as can be easily derived from (24.1), ψ satisfies the equation

$$\Delta\psi_t + U\Delta\psi_x + V\Delta\psi_y + u\Delta\Psi_y + v\Delta\Psi_y = \nu\Delta\Delta\psi \tag{24.2}$$

We shall restrict ourselves to a simple type of flow, called *shear flow*, described by

$$\Psi = \Psi(y), \qquad U = U(y), \qquad V = 0 \tag{24.3}$$

This flow is not consistent with equation (24.2) unless Ψ gives a Couette or Poiseuille flow (cf. pp. 148-149). We may assume though that the variation of Ψ with respect to x is small enough to be neglected. Equation (24.2) then becomes

$$\Delta\psi_t + U\Delta\psi_x - U_{yy}\psi_x = \nu\Delta\Delta\psi \tag{24.4}$$

Let the main flow given by Ψ be restricted to a channel: $y_1 \leqq y \leqq y_2$.
The main flow should then satisfy the boundary conditions

$$\Psi = \text{const.}, \qquad U = 0 \quad \text{for } y = y_1, y_2 \tag{24.5}$$

while the disturbed flow ψ should satisfy the condition

$$\psi = u = 0 \quad \text{for } y = y_1, y_2 \tag{24.6}$$

As before, we take ψ to be a simple wave motion, i.e. of the form

$$\psi = h(t, y)\,e^{i\alpha x} \tag{24.7}$$

This restriction is justified since every solution can be represented by the superposition of such wave motions. Substituting (24.7) in (24.4) we obtain

$$(h_{yy} - \alpha^2 h)_t + i\alpha U[h_{yy} - \alpha^2 h] - i\alpha U_{yy} h = \nu[h_{yyyy} - 2\alpha^2 h_{yy} + \alpha^4 h] \tag{24.8}$$

together with the boundary conditions

$$h = h_y = 0 \quad \text{at } y = y_1, y_2 \tag{24.9}$$

At the time $t = 0$ an initial disturbance

$$h = h_0(y)$$

is prescribed. It is clear that a solution h of (24.8) depends on α and that it is sufficient to assume $\alpha \geqq 0$ since for $\alpha < 0$ we may set

$$h(t, y, -\alpha) = \overline{h(t, y, \alpha)}$$

The question of stability or instability can be resolved if we can prove either that for all initial disturbances the motion dies out or that there is an initial disturbance for which the motion increases. In the first case the main flow is stable while in the second case it is unstable with respect to wave disturbances of wave length $2\pi/\alpha$. We refer to these two situations respectively as α-stability and α-instability. We consider normal modes of motion

$$h(t, y) = f(y) e^{\beta t} \tag{24.10}$$

and we assume that every motion can be obtained by superposition of such motions. Although, as could be shown, this is not true for perfect fluid flow we assume it temporarily. If for a particular value of α, we have $\operatorname{Re}\beta < 0$ for all possible values of β we have α-stability; if there is one β such that $\operatorname{Re}\beta > 0$ we have α-instability. The border between stability and instability is characterized by $\operatorname{Re}\beta = 0$. It is convenient to write

$$\beta = -i\alpha c \qquad c = c' + ic'' \tag{24.11}$$

Since $\alpha \geq 0$ we have α-*stability* whenever all $c'' < 0$ and α-*instability* if there is one $c'' > 0$. A "neutral" mode characterized by $\operatorname{Re}\beta = 0$ occurs when $c'' = 0$, i.e. when c is real. In the last case the motion with the stream function

$$\psi = f(y) e^{i\alpha(x-ct)}$$

can be considered as a progressing wave with phase velocity c.

The problem for the normal modes is to find "characteristic" values of c for a given α so that equation (24.8) with boundary conditions (24.9) has a solution when $h(t, y)$ is assumed to be of the form $h(t, y) = f(y) e^{\beta t}$. In this case equation (24.8) becomes

$$(U-c)(f_{yy}-\alpha^2 f) - U_{yy}f = \frac{\nu}{i\alpha}(f_{yyyy}-2\alpha^2 f_{yy}+\alpha^4 f) \tag{24.12}$$

Equation (24.12) is known as the Sommerfeld-Orr equation. The boundary conditions (24.9) become

$$f = f_y = 0 \quad \text{at } y = y_1, y_2 \tag{24.13}$$

Considerable work has been done on the stability problem connected with this equation. We shall report about the most important results without giving details. The history of this work is rather complex and cannot be unravelled here. An excellent account of the earlier work, which apparently was initiated by Rayleigh, is found in the report by Synge. A new approach was made by Prandtl's school. After significant contribution by Heisenberg (1922), very striking definite facts were discovered by Tollmien (1922). The theoretical predictions were verified experimentally by Schubauer and Skramstad (1947). Significant classification was achieved by C. C. Lin (1945), who also developed a somewhat more manageable approach. A mathematically rigorous theory of various questions involved was given by Wasow (1948, 1952).

Let us first consider the limiting case of a perfect fluid. In this case, equation (24.12) reduces to

$$(U-c)(f_{yy}-\alpha^2 f)-U_{yy}f = 0 \qquad (24.14)$$

with the boundary conditions

$$f = 0 \quad \text{at } y = y_1, y_2 \qquad (24.14)'$$

the boundary conditions $f_y = 0$ at y_1, y_2 are lost.

Suppose that this problem has a solution $f = f_1(y)$ with $c = c_1$. If c_1 is not real we say that a non-neutral mode exists. If $c_1'' = \text{Im } c_1 > 0$ the shear flow is said to be α-unstable. If $c_1'' < 0$ the function $f_2(y) = \overline{f_1(y)}$ is a solution with $c_2 = \bar{c}_1$ and hence with $c_2'' > 0$. Again, we conclude that the shear flow is unstable. We may thus formulate

Theorem I. If a non-neutral mode exists for a certain value of α, the shear flow is α-unstable.

One must be careful, however, in drawing conclusions from this statement about the stability of shear flows of a viscous fluid. Naturally, one is inclined to consider a solution $f(y)$ of the reduced equation (24.14) as an approximation to a solution of the full equation (24.12) except near the endpoints. This would be justified if a solution of equations (24.12), (24.13) existed which is arbitrarily close to the solution $f(y)$ of (24.14). Whether or not this is so requires a closer investigation. The results of this investigation derived by C. C. Lin (and proved rigorously by W. Wasow) is that a solution $f(y)$ of the unreduced equations (24.12), (24.13) does approximate solutions of the reduced equations (24.14) if $c'' > 0$ but not if $c'' < 0$. This fact may seem surprising, in particular, since any solution $f_2(y)$ of (24.14) with $c_2'' > 0$ leads to a solution $f_1(y) = \overline{f_2(y)}$ with $c_1'' = -c_2'' < 0$. The same is, however, not true for the solution of the unreduced equations (24.12),

(24.13). For as Lin has pointed out if $f(y)$ satisfies (24.12) then $f(y)$ satisfies the equation which differs from (24.12) in the sign of the right member, which in general does not vanish. Note that we have assumed $\alpha > 0$.

It follows from these remarks that the statement of Theorem 1 remains valid for fluids with a sufficiently small viscosity. For the instability of the shear flow depends on the existence of a solution of (24.12), (24.13) with $c'' > 0$ and this existence is guaranteed if such a solution of (24.14) exists.

Simple and significant criteria were given by Rayleigh and Tollmien for the existence or absence of non-neutral modes. These criteria depend on whether or not the velocity profile $U(y)$ has a "flex", i.e. a point of inflection at which the second derivative $U_{yy}(y)$ changes sign.

Theorem 2. Should a velocity profile $U(y)$ have no flex in an interval $y_1 < y < y_2$ then no non-neutral mode exists.

To prove this we assume the contrary, i.e. we suppose that a non-neutral mode exists. Then there is a solution $f(y)$ of equations (24.14) and (24.14)' for which c is not real. Multiplying (24.14) by $-\bar{f}(y)/(U-c)$ and integrating we obtain

$$\int_{y_1}^{y_2} \bar{f} \left\{ -f_{yy} + \alpha^2 f + \frac{U_{yy}}{U-c} f \right\} dy = 0$$

Integration by parts of the last equation yields

$$\int_{y_1}^{y_2} |f_y|^2 + \alpha^2 |f|^2 + \frac{U_{yy}}{U-c} |f|^2 \, dy = 0$$

The imaginary part of the last relation must vanish. It is

$$c'' \int_{y_1}^{y_2} \frac{U_{yy}}{|U-c|^2} |f|^2 \, dy = 0$$

Hence the assumption that c'' does not vanish leads to a contradiction since by hypothesis U_{yy} does not change sign. This result shows that for velocity profiles which are convex the only possible normal modes are neutral. Poiseuille flows and Blasius flows, that is, the flows in the boundary layer past a flat plate have such convex velocity profiles.

Shear flow in a non-viscous fluid is therefore stable if the velocity profile has no flex. One is tempted to conclude from this result that shear flow with a flexless velocity profile is stable also in a viscous fluid since one should expect that the viscosity should have a stabilizing rather than destabilizing effect. Such a conclusion would, however, be quite wrong, as we shall discuss in detail later on.

We proceed to discuss the existence of neutral modes and their properties in case the velocity profile possesses a flex. We first note that the function

$$f(y) = U(y) - c$$

is a neutral mode with $\alpha = 0$ if the constant c can be so chosen that $U(y) - c$ satisfies the boundary condition. Otherwise, it can be seen that the value c for any neutral mode is either complex, in which case

$$U_{min} \leqq c' \leqq U_{max}$$

or real where $c = U(y^*)$ with y^* the value of y for which $U_{yy}(y^*) = 0$. The latter statement is derived from the differential equation although it does not follow immediately from it.

It is not difficult to see that a value of α exists for which there is a neutral mode. If $c = U(y^*)$ we assume that the function

$$q(y) = \frac{U_{yy}(y)}{U(y) - c}$$

is regular at $y = y^*$ which of course presupposes that $U_{yy}(y^*) = 0$. Then we consider the eigenvalue problem

$$-f_{yy} + q(y)f = \lambda f$$

with the boundary condition (24.14)'. Since q is regular this eigenvalue problem possesses an infinite sequence of eigenvalues. Moreover, it possesses one negative eigenvalue $\lambda = -\alpha_0^2$. In order to show this it is sufficient to observe that the ratio

$$\int_{y_1}^{y_2} [|f_y|^2 + q(y)|f|^2]\, dy \Big/ \int_{y_1}^{y_2} |f|^2\, dy$$

can be made negative, namely, by the function

$$f = U(y)$$

assuming that $U(y)$ satisfies the boundary conditions (24.14)'.

It was further shown by Tollmien that for values of α different from α_0, in fact, for values $\alpha < \alpha_0$, a non-neutral mode exists. Automatically,

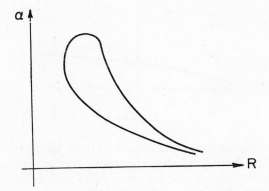

Fig. 24.1. Case of Profile without Flex.

$c'' > 0$ for this mode so that the shear flow in non-viscous fluid is unstable for such values of α. It has further been shown that in the neighborhood of a neutral mode we can always find a flow which is unstable.

We now consider the full problem given by (24.12) and (24.13) and plot the value of α corresponding to a given value of v for which c is real. We then obtain two curves depending on whether the velocity profile has a flex or not. The resulting curves described by Fig. 24.1, Fig. 24.2 are transition curves for regions of stability and instability.

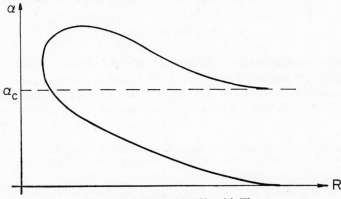

Fig. 24.2. Case of Profile with Flex.

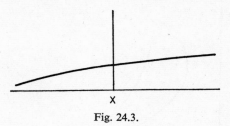

Fig. 24.3.

In certain experiments conducted by G. B. Schubauer and H. K. Skramstad[1] the above results have been confirmed experimentally in the case of the boundary layer of the viscous flow past a flat plate (Blasius flow) (cf. Fig. 24.3). It was noted that with increasing Reynolds number

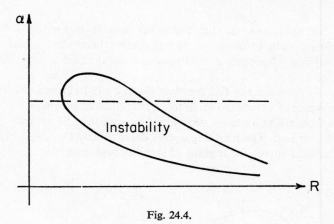

Fig. 24.4.

the initial oscillations are first damped until the mode becomes neutral then they are amplified until the mode becomes neutral again, finally they are damped again. It was noticed that the greatest amplification occurs shortly before the mode becomes neutral for the second time.

[1] Cf. Schubauer and Skramstad: *Laminar Boundary-Layer Oscillations and Transition on a Flat Plate*—Research Paper RP 1772—National Bureau of Standards.

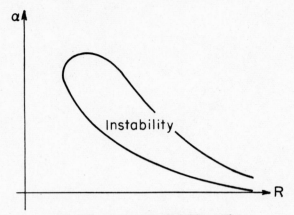

Fig. 24.5. Case of Profile without Flex.

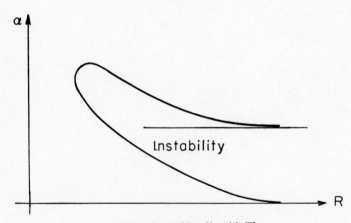

Fig. 24.6. Case of Profile with Flex.